About the authors

Dr Christopher Green MB, BCh, Fʀ.ᴀᴄᴘ**, ᴍʀᴄᴘ(UK), FRCP(I), DCH**

Christopher Green is a specialist paediatrician, Head of the Child Development Unit at the Royal Alexandra Hospital for Children, Sydney and clinical lecturer at the University of Sydney. Over the last 15 years Dr Green has been prominent in introducing modern attitudes towards treatment of ADD to Australia.

He is the well known author of two bestseller books on child-care, *Toddler Taming* (1984, 1990) and *Babies!* (1988). Dr Green runs parenting seminars which reach over 20,000 Australian and New Zealand parents every year. He is a columnist with the *Australian Women's Weekly* and formerly a regular presenter with Australia's top rating, day-time television program, the 'Midday Show'.

Chris is married to Hilary, a part-time general practitioner and full-time mum. They have two teenage sons. When not working he enjoys sailing, swimming and outdoors Australia with his family.

Dr Kit Y Chee MB, BS, FRACP

Kit Chee is a specialist paediatrician. She is Clinical Research Fellow at the Child Development Unit at the Royal Alexandra Hospital for Children, Sydney.

Kit has a special interest in children's learning, language, ADD and the effect of stimulants. Kit is married to Arthur, also a paediatrician. Outside work every minute is taken up looking after her two young children, but she still finds time to enjoy classical music, the arts and exploring Sydney's harbour foreshores.

Cleveland Tertiary College

Understanding Attention Deficit

Dr Christopher Green

DR KIT CHEE

VERMILION
LONDON

Important note

The author's work is not intended to be exhaustive and matters of opinion are often expressed. This book describes conditions commonly presented and it is not intended that this work be substituted for the benefits obtained from the consultation with, and treatment by, a professional practitioner. Where drugs or prescriptions are referred to care should be taken to note same in conjunction with specifications issued from time to time by the relevant drug houses.

First published in the UK in 1995

3 5 7 9 10 8 6 4

Text Copyright © Dr Christopher Green, 1994
Illustrations Copyright © Roger Roberts, 1994

Dr Christopher Green has asserted his moral right to be identified as the author of this work in accordance with the Copyright, Design and patents Act 1988.

First published in the United Kingdom in 1995 by Vermilion
an imprint of Ebury Press
Random House UK Ltd
Random House
20 Vauxhall Bridge Road
London SW1V 2SA

Random House UK Limited Reg. No. 954009

A CIP catalogue record for this book is available from the British Library

ISBN 0 09 180844 8

Typeset by SX Composing Ltd, Rayleigh, Essex
Printed and bound in Great Britain by Butler & Tanner Ltd, Frome and London

Papers used by Vermilion are natural, recyclable products made from wood grown in sustainable forests.

Contents

Foreword

Many parents and professionals, having just picked up this book will be wondering if ADD is just another trendy trans-Atlantic condition. I sympathise with you. Previously I too thought this was an unimportant over-rated diagnosis. However, after years of working closely with families and children, I am now convinced this is both important and under-diagnosed.

As a Consultant Paediatrician working in the UK, it seems amazing that a condition which is said to severely disadvantage at least 2% of North American and Australian school children, is rarely recognised in Europe. Some colleagues suggest that all those restless, inattentive, impulsive genes were shipped off to the New World, but it's not that simple—we must be missing something that is of real importance.

The idea of ADD did not originate in the United States. In fact, the first reliable description was made in England. In the early 1900s, George Still, a famous London paediatrician, described a group of children who caused great trouble in his practice. He felt these difficult behaviours were part of the child's temperamental make-up and not caused by poor parenting. Still found these ADD-like children were hard to treat.

After the British alerted the world to this condition, it was the North Americans who undertook most of the follow-up. In the US, ADD was said to be caused by a difference in the fine tuning of the child's brain and was treated by behavioural techniques as well as medication. Meanwhile the Europeans had a more analytical view of ADD, with the symptoms blamed on problems in parental attitudes or the home.

The book, *Understanding Attention Deficit Disorder*, comes from the work of the UK trained Dr Christopher Green. When he moved to Australia in the early 1980s he found most psychologists and psychiatrists followed his European view of ADD. But this did not help with the 'out of step' children that came to his practice. In desperation, he looked to the North American work and found their treatment brought great success.

As Dr Green 'saw the light', the ideas in this book were developing. He became aware of the immense stress these children could bring to their families. Teachers were amazed that these intelligent children achieved so little at school. It became apparent that many of these children's parents had suffered ADD themselves when young. Many of these adults still secretly believed they were inferior, though talented and intelligent. Dr Green found that the behavioural techniques that worked so well in his bestselling book *Toddler Taming* were largely ineffective in ADD children. There was also a reluctant acceptance that stimulant medication could often bring about amazing changes.

Throughout the 1980s, Dr Green and his colleagues met more than their fair share of criticism. Their ideas were said to be controversial and medication dangerous. When they removed the blame from parents, they were said to be colluding with these mums and dads and by lifting the guilt, prevented them from facing up to their responsibility in causing the child's problem.

But all this changed in the 1990s. The ADD revolution that hit the Antipodes did not come from the work of paediatricians, educators, psychologists or psychiatrists. It came from parents who knew their children had been created with a problem and insisted that the professionals look at things in a new light. They set up parent support groups who insisted on up to date management from doctors, psychologists and the schools.

Through the efforts of these parents ADD is now widely recognised and well managed. Now doctors, educators, psychologists and psychiatrists are all trained in the modern view of ADD and its treatment. The ideas to be found in the book *Understanding Attention Deficit Disorder* reflect what is now accepted in most of the North American and Australian scene. What you will find in this book comes from Dr Green's own experience and is greatly added to by the research input of his co-author, Dr Kit Chee.

At this time ADD must be causing as much pain to children and families in the UK as it is elsewhere in the world. Europe must be about to experience an inevitable explosion of interest in this all too common condition. This book is authoritative, easy to read and up to date. Let's hope that it may act as the catalyst which sets this revolution in motion.

Dr Geoff Kewley, Consultant Paediatrician
Learning Assessment Centre, The Ashdown Hospital

Authors' Note

The term ADD is used throughout this book, although we realise that Attention Deficit Hyperactivity Disorder (ADHD) is a more correct label. We use the term ADD as it has popular acceptance with parents and professionals at the time of writing.

Introduction

Whilst most professionals in Australia have now accepted Attention Deficit Disorder (ADD) as an important condition of childhood, this is still not the case in the UK. ADD causes clever children to underfunction at school and, despite good parents, to behave poorly at home. With the current awareness of ADD, professionals and parents are shouting out for practical advice on how to help these children and, therefore, their families as well. This book aims to fulfil that need.

Understanding Attention Deficit Order presents a clear overview of a far from simple condition. The authors teach thousands of parents about ADD every year and have a special interest in finding practical ways to help common problems. Chris Green writes with the benefit of years experience working with families with ADD children. Kit Chee's practical experience is supplemented by her research interest, shaped by monitoring of the latest international literature and visits to top medical and educational research centres in North America.

The book provides an easy to read text, full of well-tried, practical suggestions that work in both the home and classroom. For those who wish to take it further, the appendixes in Part Three are full of additional information, such as summaries of the most recent research findings, current diagnostic criteria, parent–teacher questionnaires, and suggestions to improve language, handwriting and sport skills. The content is designed to suit the needs of parents as well as the most information-hungry professional.

We emphasise that this book is focused on our special area of interest, the younger ADD child with difficult behaviour. Certainly, before they become teenagers, we believe that ADD children may be annoying, but they are basically good kids, who just don't think. We do realise that some ADD children can move on to develop Oppositional Defiant Disorder or Conduct Disorder behaviour, but management of these difficult conditions is outside the brief of this book.

As we write, there is still debate over the exact incidence of ADD, the best diagnostic method, the relative importance of various therapies and the long-term benefits of stimulant medication. These unresolved issues are unimportant as long as we all pursue the same goal—to help the child with ADD to enter adulthood with the best possible education, good self-confidence, useful life skills and intact family relationships. If we all work together towards this end, the next decade will be a lot easier for these children and their much maligned parents.

This book gives a very personal perspective and there will be people who dispute some of our ideas. All we ask is that if you can relate to the text and it helps a child in your care, please read on.

Christopher Green
Kit Chee

PART 1

Understanding ADD

1

ADD—the Facts

Attention Deficit Disorder (ADD) is not new: it was first described almost 100 years ago, and the beneficial effects of stimulant medication have been well known for over half a century.

Today when we talk about ADD we refer to a troublesome cluster of behaviours that cause a child to underachieve academically and to behave poorly, despite having a good intellect and receiving quality parenting. The behaviours now known as ADD were once called hyperactivity, then Attention Deficit Disorder and now, if we are going to be completely correct, they should be labelled Attention Deficit Hyperactivity Disorder.

With so much current interest in ADD one might think that we are in the midst of an epidemic. But ADD is occurring no more frequently than in the past, we have just become more skilful at recognising a very real condition that previously was missed and mis-diagnosed.

Despite our better knowledge of ADD, many children with ADD remain undiagnosed. Bewildered parents watch as their children underachieve at school and create immense tension in the home. Professionals are often equally unaware, some continuing to believe ADD to be a trendy non-condition or a poor excuse for incompetent parenting.

A few of the old school of child psychiatrists still see ADD as a sign of the dysfunction and troubled mind of the child's parents. Fortunately, parent punishing is well on the wane with entrenched ideas being overtaken by science.

ADD is caused by a subtle difference in the fine tuning of the normal brain. The seeds of ADD are present at birth. The extent of the difficulty depends on the severity of the child's problem and how well their behaviour and education are managed. We can't change this inborn predisposition, but we can most certainly modify the home and school environment to help our children behave and achieve to their maximum potential.

The facts about ADD

With so much misinformation still confusing today's parents, let's start this book by stating some important facts:

- ADD is a real condition which mildly affects up to 10 per-cent of all children, 2 per cent of children being severely disadvantaged.

- The peak time for the majority of parents to ask for help is after the child starts school. Most ADD children come to attention in the junior school years. This challenges the old idea that hyperactivity is a problem of three-year-olds.

- ADD is mostly a 'boy problem'. Boys are six times more likely to be referred for help than girls. (It is suggested the true ratio in the community is actually 3:1. Many girls remain undiagnosed as they tend to suffer more silently than boisterous boys.)

- ADD is caused by a minor dysfunction in the normal brain. This mild difference has now been shown conclusively using the latest brain-scanning techniques, for example, Positron Emission Tomography (PET).

- ADD refers to a reasonably consistent cluster of behaviours that include inattention, impulsivity, overactivity, insatiability, disorganisation and social clumsiness.

- The cut-off point between a normal but difficult tempera-ment and ADD is unclear. In our practice we take these ADD-like behaviours seriously only when they cause prob-lems. A problem is only a problem when it causes a problem.

- ADD is usually a hereditary condition. Most ADD children have a close relative (usually male) affected to some degree by the same problem.

- Pure ADD is usually transmitted to the child as pure ADD. ADD with specific learning disabilities, for example, ADD plus developmental reading disorder (dyslexia), usually appears in the next generation in the same combination.

- ADD is a chronic problem which affects learning and be-haviour as the child matures. Its presentation will change but the problems will continue to cause trouble throughout the school years.

- Sixty per cent of ADD children will carry some of their different behaviours with them into adulthood. Many of the world's most famous innovators, entrepreneurs and high profile people suffer from ADD.

- There is no one reliable test to diagnose ADD. With the lack of objectivity in diagnosis it is no wonder that the pronounced incidence of ADD varies greatly from expert to expert.

- Studies have shown that when the same assessor looks at children from different countries and races, the incidence of ADD is found to be equally common.

- Over half the children who present with ADD are also troubled by specific learning disabilities, for example, dyslexia, language disorder or a weakness with mathematics.

- Many preschoolers are incorrectly labelled as hyperactive. In fact, they have no problem other than the normal 'busyness' and lack of commonsense one can find at this young age.

- The most common statement from teachers upon the child entering school is, 'This child is distractible and disruptive.'

- Lack of attention (inattention) causes school children to underfunction. They find it hard to complete work unless they are stood over and given one-to-one supervision.

- Teachers are often confused as to why a child of advanced intellect can function and behave so poorly.

- Playground behaviour is frequently a problem. At school the ADD child is often known by all but liked by few.

- Parents find messages go in one ear and out the other. These children are often hard to reach and have poor short-term memories.

- Most ADD children have the social and emotional maturity of a child two-thirds their age. Lack of commonsense is a frequent complaint.

- ADD children generate great stress for those around them through the intensity of their nagging and interrogation. The stress they create makes them much more difficult for teachers and parents to manage.

- Poor impulse control leaves these children both verbally and physically accident-prone. They frequently trip, fall, act stupidly and find 'a foot in their mouth'.

- Parents often feel bewildered and uncertain why this one child stands out from the rest. Most parents feel inadequate and that they are in some way to blame.

- Treatment of ADD comes on many fronts. This includes putting in place and maintaining structures, reducing stress, avoiding confrontations, using behavioural techniques, esteem boosting and the use of stimulant medication.

- Diet does not cause ADD but has a small part to play in the management of ADD.

- The beneficial effects of stimulant medication have frequently been misrepresented by the media and by misinformed professionals. When stimulant medication is used correctly it is both safe and remarkably free of side-effects. It is without doubt the single most effective form of therapy for the child with significant ADD problems.

Diagnosis and treatment are important

ADD must be recognised and treated properly. If this does not happen it will continue to severely disadvantage tens of thousands of our children. What is worse, poorly managed ADD can lead to serious long-term problems:

- Most children with undiagnosed ADD feel inferior and believe that they are dumb.

- With academic and social failure comes shattered self-esteem.

- Children who are poorly managed in their early school years lose their drive to succeed and the will to learn.

- Family relationships can be irretrievably damaged by the stress of living with an ADD child. Many parents feel guilty when they start to wonder if they have any loving feelings for their child.

- The poorly managed ADD child has a great chance of entering their adult life badly educated, socially inept and lacking in confidence.

- Those ADD children who make a successful transition into adulthood often channel their immense drive, determination and single-mindedness to be outstanding in business or public life. We need to follow their lead and, for all ADD children, to turn their difference into an advantage.

ADD needs to be taken seriously. It is no longer good enough for parents, psychologists, teachers and paediatricians to pretend it is a trivial non-condition. Whatever means we use, our aim should be to help these children enter adulthood with the best education, esteem, and life skills that are possible. It is also vital to keep family relationships intact. If we miss out here, all the rest of our efforts are pretty pointless.

2

ADD—An Old Condition Rediscovered

Attention Deficit Disorder is not a new condition. Churchill, Einstein and some of the most influential people of all time had one thing in common: they channelled their ADD activity, drive and single-mindedness to achieve greatness.

The history of ADD

ADD was first described almost 100 years ago here in the UK. Some of the earliest work on ADD was done by a famous English paediatrician, George Still. He remains a respected father figure who is now remembered, not for his work on

ADD, but for his classic description of arthritis in children, which continues to be called Still's disease.

Others had noticed the behaviours of ADD some years before, but it was Still, who, in 1902, was the first to recognise and describe the condition. He noticed a group of his patients, mostly boys, had difficult behaviours which had started before the age of eight. Most were inattentive, overactive and were different from other children in their resistance to discipline.

Still described these children as having a poor control of inhibition, being full of aggression and, in his Victorian language, suffering from, 'A lack of moral control.' Still saw this as a chronic condition, biological (inborn) in nature and not caused by poor parenting or adverse environment. What George Still described at the turn of the century is probably what would nowadays be called ADD with Oppositional Defiant Disorder (ODD) or Conduct Disorder (CD) (see Appendix XVIII: General Reviews on ADD; Barkley, R.A.).

It is interesting to note that at this time the United Kingdom led the world in its understanding of ADD. Unfortunately, as the twentieth century moved along, British researchers became preoccupied with a more psychoanalytical style of psychiatry, which left the job of sorting out ADD to the North Americans.

ADD and brain damage

Interest in ADD came next in the wake of the great influenza epidemic of 1918–19. This epidemic killed over 20 million people worldwide, and its associated encephalitis (an inflammation of the brain) left many people neurologically impaired. Some of these people went on to develop Parkinson's disease in later life, while others showed immediate signs of brain dysfunction that had some similarities to the problems first described by Still. From this experience, ADD was now seen as being the result of brain damage.

It was a long time before this injured brain idea lost favour and research returned to the inbuilt, biological nature initially suggested by Still.

Stimulants and ADD—A chance finding

In 1937 a group of institutionalised children was subjected to an unorthodox treatment. They were given the drug amphetamine and to everybody's surprise their difficult behaviours improved. It took almost another 20 years before stimulant medication became widely used, but this chance finding was to greatly influence the direction of future treatment.

Minimal brain damage—minimal brain dysfunction

Researchers in the 1950s and 1960s began to realise that most ADD children had never suffered any brain damage. They softened the name then used to describe ADD behaviours from Minimal Brain Damage to Minimal Brain Dysfunction. This implied that the brain was effectively normal, but there was some subtle malfunction which accounted for the ADD behaviours. Paediatricians then became obsessed with hunting for minor neurological differences. Until relatively recent times much of the assessment of ADD looked at the flow of movement in the fingers, the dominance of eye, foot and hand and a multitude of other trivial tests. This form of assessment is still popular in some North American centres, but most have moved on from this unhelpful preoccupation with 'soft neurological signs'.

Minimal Brain Dysfunction was never a satisfactory term, but at least it implied that ADD was made up of a cluster of behaviours and it placed the blame on the brain, rather than the parents.

Hyperkinesis and hyperactivity

During the time when the term Minimal Brain Dysfunction (MBD) was being used, other medical professionals were starting to look at specific behaviours. In the early 1960s the hyperactive child syndrome was first described. The symptoms were somewhat unclear, but the condition was seen as being part of the child's individual make-up and not caused by brain damage. Through the 1960s and 1970s the terms MBD and hyperactivity were both used, hyperactivity being the name that caught the attention of the public and the press.

Hyperactivity and the Feingold Diet

Dr Ben Feingold, a former Professor of Allergy in San Francisco, first suggested a relationship between diet and hyperactivity in 1973. He claimed that the reported rates of hyperactivity were increasing in proportion to the number of additives which legally polluted food. Feingold was quickly championed by the press and such was the overreaction, the American Government was obliged to set up committees to investigate the claims.

Feingold believed that 50 per cent of hyperactive children might be helped by his diet. When the results of carefully controlled trials were analysed, it appeared that no more than 5 per cent of ADD children were adversely affected by food. (See Chapter 10 for an up-to-date overview of diet and ADD.)

Years of obsessive interest in diet distracted attention from the complex package of problems that made up ADD, and the already well-proven benefits of stimulant medication.

Stimulants—in and out of fashion

The beneficial effects of stimulant medication have been well known for over half a century. The benefits of amphetamines were clearly documented in the late 1930s, but stimulants were not widely used until the late 1950s and 1960s. The main breakthrough came with the introduction in 1957 of a new stimulant—Methylphenidate (Ritalin). In the next decade many carefully controlled studies showed that stimulants were both safe and effective.

The use of stimulants increased rapidly, impeded only by the occasional beat-up in the media. In one early 1970s article, that is still often quoted, the rate of prescribing was misrepresented by 10 times its correct level. This media misinformation helped the sale of newspapers but it also frightened parents from a form of therapy that for some would have revolutionised their relationship with their children.

The greatest assault on stimulants was made in the late 1980s from an unexpected source, the Church of Scientology. This organisation set up a lobby group which sent press statements to the media under the impressive title of 'the Citizens' Commission on Human Rights'. Most of their activities took place in the United States, although the group's actions also affected many families in Australia.

Newspapers and radio stations were quick to transmit the Commission's dramatic claims. Ritalin, it was asserted, was a dangerous and addictive drug, often used as a chemical straitjacket to subdue normally exuberant children because of intolerant educators, parents and money-hungry psychiatrists. Ritalin could result in violence, murder, suicide, Tourette's syndrome, permanent brain damage, emotional disturbance, seizures, high blood pressure, confusion, agitation and depression. Great controversy was said to exist among the scientific and professional communities concerning the use of medication (see Appendix XVIII: General Reviews on ADD; Barkley, R.A.)

This unexpected assault by a religious subgroup set back the appropriate treatment of ADD by years. Parents believed what they read in the press and refused to put their children on the medication. Even worse was the attitude of many top educationalists, psychologists, psychiatrists, paediatricians and policymakers. They were swayed by what they saw in the media rather than reviewing the hundreds of studies in the scientific literature.

It was only at the start of the 1990s that we were able to shake off these antistimulant attitudes. In the meantime, thousands of children have been prevented from receiving the treatment they needed.

From hyperactivity to Attention Deficit Disorder

In the early 1970s, a Canadian, Virginia Douglas promoted the view that attention deficit was a more important symptom than hyperactivity. By the end of the 1970s her publications were so impressive that the American Psychiatric Association in 1980 used the term 'Attention Deficit Disorder' in their diagnostic and statistic manual (DSM-III). In 1987 the American Psychiatric Association put out DSM-III-Revised, which now talked of Attention Deficit Hyperactivity Disorder. In 1994 the Association released its latest classification DSM-IV, which describes Attention Deficit Hyperactivity Disorder (ADHD) without active, impulsive behaviours; ADHD with active, impulsive behaviours, as well as some ADHD combinations of both. Most parents, teachers and legislators now use the popular term

ADD, but to be strictly correct these behaviours should be referred to as ADHD.

Conclusion

Our definition of ADD has progressed from Still's cluster of behaviours which were of biological (inborn) origin and had a poor prognosis. This was followed by a time of presumed brain damage. Next all the focus was on hyperactivity, a concept still prevalent in the UK today. Then diet seemed all important in a condition that was believed to resolve itself before high school age. The current definition describes a cluster of inbuilt behaviours of which inattention is paramount and impulsivity and overactivity are usual. The condition is chronic and symptoms often continue into adulthood. Medication is now accepted as an important part of therapy.

We have come a long way, but ADD remains a highly variable, complex and poorly defined condition. The danger for today's parents and professionals is to become lost in the uncertainties, rather than focusing on what we know to be true and using this to help our children.

Summary: one hundred years of ADD

1902:   Clear description of ADD behaviours.
                Not caused by brain damage or poor parenting.
1930s: Brain damage causes ADD behaviours.
1937:   Stimulant medication first used in ADD.
1950s, 60s: ADD believed to be a brain dysfunction. 'Minimal Brain Dysfunction'.
                Psychoanalytical child psychiatrists see ADD in terms of parent and environment problem (for some this attitude continued until the 1990s).

1957:	Methylphenidate (Ritalin) introduced.
1960–70:	The 'Hyperactive Child Syndrome' becomes popular. Ritalin widely used and many research papers on stimulants.
1970–75:	Inaccurate media claims raise concerns with medication. Feingold Diet becomes popular.
1975–80:	Medication regains considerable popularity.
1980:	American Psychiatric Association uses term 'Attention Deficit Disorder' (DSM-III).
1987:	American Psychiatric Association uses term 'Attention Deficit Hyperactivity Disorder' (DSM-IIIR).
1987:	Anti-medication media campaign misleads many authoritative Australians.
1990:	Positron Emission Tomography (PET Scan) shows significant difference between the function of the ADD and non-ADD brain.
1994:	American Psychiatric Association redefines 'Attention Deficit Hyperactivity Disorder' DSM-IV.

3

ADD—the Cause

Researchers still disagree on the exact cause of ADD, but two things are certain. First, it is an hereditary condition. Second, the problems of ADD result from a subtle difference in the fine tuning of the brain.

Most of the current debate centres around the exact nature of this brain difference. Some doctors see ADD as a part of the normal spectrum of temperament, but the majority believe that it is a syndrome which is separate from temperament. Most researchers now believe that it is due to the underfunctioning of those areas of the brain that put the brakes on unwise behaviour, the *frontal lobes*. In addition to this, there seems to exist an unusual imbalance in the message-transmitting chemicals of the brain, the *neurotransmitters*.

Whatever the rights and wrongs of these theories, two old ideas have certainly outlived their day: ADD is definitely not caused by diet or poor parenting.

Heredity/genes and ADD

When we look carefully at families in our practice, we notice most children with ADD seem to have a close relative with a similar problem. Often we see a father who found his early school years difficult or who underfunctioned academically for his abilities. Some ADD adults have done well in life but are still restless and inattentive, and are fitted with a dangerously short fuse.

There is good research evidence to back up the belief in a genetic influence. Identical twins are useful to study, as they are created sharing the same genetic material. If one twin suffers ADD, research shows an almost 90 per cent chance the other will also have this problem.

Unidentical twins have the same risk of ADD as the brother or sister of any ADD child. The risk between siblings is somewhere between 30 and 40 per cent depending on who you believe. These are high figures when compared with the rate of ADD in the general population, which is somewhere between 2 and 10 per cent. An ADD child of a parent with both ADD and dyslexia usually inherits both the attentional and reading problems together.

There is no doubt that genes play an important part in the inheritance of both ADD and specific learning disabilities (for example dyslexia), but why one child in a family gets ADD and another does not, remains a mystery.

The brain difference

In this noisy world, most of the unimportant messages that come into the brain are screened out at a low level without ever coming to the attention of 'middle management'. Important information is taken in and looked at by the specialist parts of the brain, which interact together to give a properly coordinated response. Finally, the chief executive (frontal lobe) takes an overview of the middle management decisions, approving or disapproving on the grounds of appropriateness, priorities, future implications and their effect on others.

In the ADD child's brain it seems that the information rushes in without much filtering, which leaves the television screen of the mind in a bit of a buzz. The information is integrated, but action is often taken before the chief executive has been notified.

This is an oversimplification of a complicated process, but there is no doubt that the ADD child does become overloaded with too much unfiltered stimulation and they tend to respond without giving proper consideration.

Brain research in ADD

At present the main research interest is in three areas: assessing *frontal lobe function* (the seat of executive control), studying the message transmitting *brain chemicals* (neurotransmitters), investigating *areas of under- and overfunction* (SPECT scans).

Assessing frontal lobe function—neuropsychology

A new breed of psychologists, the neuropsychologists, are constantly developing ways to study the subtle workings of the brain. One area of special interest is the executive control which resides in the frontal lobes.

Most knowledge of this part of the brain comes from studies of adult accident victims. When their frontal lobes have been injured, these people respond to situations without proper consideration. Most of the tests of frontal lobe function focus on 'response inhibition' and 'mental flexibility', as problems in these areas seem to be the hallmark of frontal lobe dysfunction.

In frontal lobe function tests the child is bombarded with a lot of distracting information and in the midst of this they are repeatedly challenged, to see if they will make a considered, not reflex, response. In the ADD child these tests show up a weakness in knowing when to react, when to hold back and when to modify their response.

The restless, impulsive ADD child is found to perform poorly in response inhibition and mental flexibility, which confirms a weakness in frontal lobe function. Children who have ADD without this impulsive package of behaviour, the 'hypoactive ADD', have an additional problem. They have the same weakness in frontal lobe function and, on top of this, neuropsychology tests show that their speed of processing information is very slow. These dreamy ADD children have frontal lobe dysfunction and also 'slow moving cogs' in their brain.

Out of tune brain chemicals — neurotransmitters' imbalance

Messages are continually moving to and from all parts of our brains. It is thought that these messages are transmitted along lines of cells, one nudging the next, which nudges the next, and so on. It is almost like a line of upturned dominoes, with one cell producing a sharp burst of chemical, which stirs the next cell, which passes it on, until the last domino drops. These chemical neurotransmitters have been extensively studied in animal experiments and are also known to be present in humans.

There are probably a number of parts to this transmittal process which are at present poorly understood. There is a stimulating chemical, probably *noradrenaline*, which excites the next cell. Then there must be an enzyme which sweeps up the excess noradrenaline from between the nerve cells to prepare for the next message. Finally, there is another chemical, probably *dopamine*, needed to dampen unwanted responses, which is always on stand-by to apply the brakes.

In ADD children there appears to be both a reduction and imbalance of these brain chemicals. It is believed that the stimulant medications Methylphenidate and Dexamphetamine in some way affect the balance of noradrenaline and dopamine, and bring a clearer focus to the ADD brain.

Brain imaging—SPECT & PET

Until recently medical methods of visualising the brain did little to help us understand ADD. Skull X-rays showed problems in the skull bones but not the brain. Routine CAT (Computer Axial Tomography) and MRI (Magnetic Resonance Imaging) scans showed the anatomy in detail, but in ADD brains this was essentially normal.

In the late 1980s two exciting new developments arrived, firstly Single Photon Emission Computed Tomography (SPECT) and then Positron Emission Tomography (PET scanning). These techniques assess the level of activity in the various parts of the brain, but they are tests of function rather than anatomy (see also Appendix VIII).

The SPECT measures blood flow to different parts of the brain and emits much less radiation than a PET scan. In one form of PET, a sugar is tagged with a radioactive marker and injected into the body. The sugar accumulates in the areas of the brain that are doing most of the work, and this is clearly shown by a PET scan.

Due to the amount of radiation of these scans and the expense, they are not generally used in children with ADD, but trialled on ADD adults and children, results of these scans have come up with some fascinating findings:

- The frontal lobes and their close connections are found to underfunction in ADD.

- The areas of the brain which collect auditory and visual input seem overloaded in ADD, suggesting that they are being bombarded by a lot of unfiltered, inappropriate information. With so much overload, it is no wonder our children can't focus their attention.

- When stimulant medication is administered, the difference seen in the brain scan of a person with ADD can be greatly reduced. This exciting finding shows that the effects of stimulant medication are certainly no figment of anyone's imagination; they can be shown to partly reverse the brain problems that cause ADD behaviours.

Parenting, as a cause of ADD

Children with ADD often behave badly and cause stress for their parents. The normal methods of discipline work less well and after some years of failure most parents back off and aim for the more peaceful path.

Some uninsightful experts, when seeing this lack of textbook discipline, misread the situation and attribute the child's behaviour to poor parental management.

It is important for every professional to realise that a child's behaviour affects the style of disciplining, just as the parent's discipline affects the style of behaviour.

Genuine parenting problems

Where major family chaos exists, this will affect any child, whether they have ADD or not. Statistics show that ADD children have a greater chance of coming from a dysfunctional home setting. On face value it would be easy to see this family turmoil as the sole cause of the difficult behaviour. But things are not always what they seem.

We know that major troubles in the home are much more likely if one parent has or both parents have an intolerant, impulsive, socially inept style of temperament. These problems of personality make an adult hard to live with, but they may also be symptoms of unresolved ADD.

This is where the confusion really starts. If a parent has ADD, the child is at risk of inheriting the same condition. If this genetically more difficult child is then brought up in a home which is inconsistent, volatile and full of stress, the behaviour will be blown through the roof.

Where major environmental chaos exists alongside ADD, it is often hard to work out which came first—the chicken or the egg. Genes and environment may both be responsible.

ADD—normal, not pathological

Research from the late 1950s shows that each child is born with an individual temperamental style. Could it be that ADD is just part of the wide spectrum of normal temperament? ADD behaviours may even have been an advantage in the past.

Until recent times, reading, writing and sitting in a classroom would have been irrelevant for the average child and ADD would probably not have been noticed. Going even further back, ADD may have been an advantage in cave-dweller times, when survival was all important. While cooking a rabbit over a fire our ADD ancestors would be quickly distracted by every breaking twig and rustle in the bushes. If danger appeared they would respond by reflex. On the other hand, our deep thinking, attentive ancestors might focus so much on the rabbit, that they would be wiped out before they knew of the danger. Possibly these active, impulsive humans were the super-humans of their day, while those who are now well-behaved school achievers would have been quite disabled.

We know that Winston Churchill underfunctioned because of his ADD, but he also rose to great heights in times of adversity. Certainly children like him have differences that can be demonstrated in the way their brain functions. ADD is not due to a damaged brain, but it is probably an edge of the wide spectrum of normal behaviours. In the past it may have been an attribute, but today the demands of school and society have turned it into a problem.

Summary: the cause of ADD
An hereditary condition

- Usually a parent or close relative has ADD.
- If a parent has ADD and SLD (Specific Learning Disabilities), the child will usually inherit both.
- In studies of identical twins, both have ADD in almost 90 per cent of cases.
- Siblings carry a 30–40 per cent risk of inheriting ADD.

A problem of fine tuning of the brain

Neuropsychology

- Impulsive ADD children show frontal lobe dysfunction: They can't 'put the brakes on'.
- Children who are inattentive without impulsive, active behaviour show the same frontal lobe problems but also have a slow processing speed: 'slow moving cogs'.

Brain chemicals

- An imbalance of noradrenaline and dopamine.
- Stimulant medication appears to help normalise this imbalance.
- This normalising effect can be demonstrated on SPECT scans.

The PET & SPECT Scans

- Frontal lobe and close connections underfunction.
- More unfiltered information arrives through ears and eyes.

Parenting and ADD

- Poor parenting does not cause ADD.
- Poor parenting can make the behaviour worse.
- Difficult children make their parents' discipline appear inadequate.
- Major family dysfunction can occur with ADD: how much is in the genes and how much in the environment?

4

ADD—the Behaviours

AND THIS IS MY DAUGHTER SARAH...

ADD is usually described as being made up of three core behaviours: *inattentiveness, impulsiveness* and *overactivity*. In addition, there is a cluster of associated behaviours which vary in their presentation: *insatiability, social clumsiness, poor coordination, disorganisation, variability, poor self-esteem* and *specific learning disabilities*.

Of the core behaviours, inattention is usually present, though it is sometimes far from obvious. Overactivity and impulsiveness come as a pair and when present they add that bit of dynamite to the behaviour. The associated behaviours, though usually there, are much more variable.

The most recent classification of ADD (DSM–IV), describes three main subtypes.

1. ADHD: *predominantly inattentive* type (dreamy, non-listening, easily distracted, inattentive, subtle learning problems).
2. ADHD: *predominantly hyperactive–impulsive* type (fidgety, restless, impulsive, impatient).
3. ADHD: *combined* type (inattentive plus the hyperactive–impulsive behaviours).

This is not the place to get into details of diagnosis. Let us first take a look at how we see the behaviours and in the next chapter try to work out how to make the diagnosis.

Inattentiveness

The inattentive child quickly loses the focus of their attention. They become bored, get distracted and may flit from task to task without achieving anything. Schoolwork takes a long time to complete or never gets finished. Teachers are mystified; the child does so much when they are stood over and so little when they are left alone.

This deficit in attention causes confusion as it varies from day to day. Some days these children seem in tune, then the next they appear 'off the planet'. This behaviour also changes from one situation to another; some of the most inattentive children we manage can leave their peers for dead as they attend to taking their bike apart or focus on a video game.

The variability of the inattention means it will often be missed by inexperienced assessors. Some ADD children appear to concentrate well in the novel, interesting environment of our offices. Some equally inattentive children work well with the psychologist in one to one testing but fall apart when they return to the busy classroom.

Inattention to verbal instructions and a poor short-term memory seem particular problems. Parents send the child off to get three things, and they appear a minute later and say, 'What was the third one?'

There is an interesting subgroup of inattentive children (ADHD—predominantly inattentive type) who are as much distracted by their own thoughts, than any noise or movement in their external environment. These children appear to drift off the air as their teacher starts to talk. Their minds are a million miles away and as they sit placidly in class they cause no one any bother, but they don't seem to learn. They become 'the quiet unachievers'. Einstein was probably one of these, an intelligent school failure who seems to have been engrossed in his own thoughts.

Adults with residual ADD often tell of their difficulty concentrating during a lecture. Others cope with their poor short-term memory by doing things immediately or writing reminder notes. Most of these inattentive adults and children have difficulty with mental arithmetic or remembering a sequence of numbers.

Inattention can really impair our communication with children. Stimulant medication has been found to help with this problem. One of our patients recently said, 'At school, when I don't take my medication, it seems that many people are talking around me. When I am on my Ritalin there is only one clear voice—that of the teacher.'

What the parents say

'What I tell him goes in one ear and out the other. Can we get his hearing tested?'

'When we work at times tables and spelling lists, they are remembered tonight but tomorrow she knows nothing.'

'He leaves a trail of lost property at school, sports fields and the pool.'

'It's not that he can't attend—he concentrates for hours, at Nintendo and watching the television.'

'She's off the air.'

'With homework I get nowhere unless I stand over him.'

'He's impossible in the morning. He goes to his room to get ready for school, half an hour later he has one sock on and is looking out the window.'

'He can remember details of what happened last year but forgets what I said two minutes ago.'

Inattention is not always ADD

When any of us find our work too difficult, we quickly lose concentration. This is called secondary inattention and is found in children who have problems of language, reading, writing or mathematics. The child switches off when their mind is overloaded, but full attention returns once the stress stops.

Children who are intellectually retarded often appear inattentive, but their attention span is appropriate for their younger developmental age. Other children drift off when their mind is preoccupied by some stress, but this comes and goes with emotional events and is not associated with the other cluster of ADD behaviours. There are, of course, occasions when emotional stress, specific learning problems and intellectual retardation can coexist with ADD.

Impulsiveness

ADD children do not set out to get into trouble, they just shoot straight from the hip with no thought of the repercussions. These children are quite aware of what is right and wrong, but it doesn't register until a millisecond after they have reacted and by then it is too late.

Cleveland Tertiary College

Poor impulse control is the behaviour that gets these children into the most trouble. Parents can't understand how someone so intelligent can behave so stupidly. No amount of reasoning helps the situation; the children are genuinely upset at what they've done but they will be just as unthinking the next time.

When the average child is shoved at assembly, they carefully check if the teacher is looking before they kick someone. The ADD child responds by reflex, gets caught and is called aggressive.

Many ADD children are accident-prone; they climb on roofs, jump out of windows, run across roads and ride their bicycles without looking ahead.

It is not unusual for lawyers to ask us to appear when they are suing an insurance company claiming that a child has become inattentive as the result of a road accident. Sometimes when we talk to the school we find that the child was just as difficult before the accident, in fact it was their inborn ADD that caused them to run across the road and get injured. One teacher even took it a step further, she told us that the bump on the head had, 'Maybe made him concentrate a bit better!'

Impulsive children interrupt and talk over the top of others. They are also easily frustrated and extremely impatient. Most have a short fuse and explode easily.

In school, incorrect answers are blurted out before the question has been completed. Instructions are only half heard before they respond. Work is rushed through with lots of careless mistakes.

In the playground, these children are easily led and often over the top. Some of the children in our care have such poor playground behaviour that they spend most lunchtimes sitting outside the principal's office. These children are not aggressive, but their behaviour quickly escalates out of control and they don't think too deeply of the consequences of their actions. A number of older children find themselves suspended from school after a poorly managed blow-up.

These sparky, 'short fuse' children are difficult to discipline as their reactions are so reflex-bound. They learn slowly from experience and along the way cause great pain to their parents, teachers and themselves. One of our colleagues says, 'Maybe we should concentrate all our efforts on teaching these children how to talk their way out of trouble—they will be constantly in it!'

What the parents say

'As a preschooler you could never trust him out of your sight.'

'He doesn't seem to learn from experience.'

'She's eight but she still interrupts us like a toddler.'

'When we visit friends, something always gets broken and somebody always gets hurt.'

'He enjoys his bike, but he has no road sense.'

'He's easily led and always gets the blame.'

'At school other children seek him out to taunt. They know they always get him to react.'

'When he's around, you never quite know what is going to happen next.'

'He's got such a short fuse—it's like juggling gelignite.'

'He's quite like his father.'

'We worry that one of these days he's going to get a driving licence!'

Overactivity

Historically, it is the hyperactive behaviour which has been the main feature of ADD. When viewed in isolation, it is our opinion that overactivity is only a minor problem, but when overactivity and impulsivity come together, this busy, short-fused combination becomes absolute dynamite.

A few of these restless young people were unusually active even before they were born. A significant number were colicky and demanding in infancy. A surprising proportion were quite average or even exceptionally good as babies—presumably they were saving themselves! For most parents the change came when they started to walk, as they took the house apart and got into everything.

Most such children are busy at preschool, finding it hard to settle at story time. Once school starts hyperactivity is generally more subtle in its presentation. There is an overall increase in body movement, which gets worse as the day wears on. These children are restless, fidget and have difficulty remaining seated. Those who appear to be sitting still are jiggling their legs, tapping their fingers or fiddling with anything they can touch. This restless squirming activity is described as 'rump hyperactivity'. These school children may not move from their seat, but their rump is certainly pretty active.

When busy children hit the playground they are like an animal released from captivity. When they return to the structure of the classroom, many find it hard to settle. At home they pace around, touch things, open and close the refrigerator door. Major overactivity tends to ease by the time they reach teen age, though some are just as wound up in adulthood.

Insatiability

Insatiability is probably the most nerve-numbing behaviour of children with ADD. Once an idea gets into their mind, they go on and on, long past the point when any other child would have let it drop.

It is a minute before dinner: 'Can I have a slice of bread?' 'No, your dinner is just about ready.' 'Can I have a biscuit?' 'No!' 'Can I have a banana?' Soon their parent is ready to scream.

They quibble, nag and rabbit on until the calmest parent is close to having a stroke. It is our experience that insatiability is the behaviour that causes the greatest stress to parents. At the end of a quiet family weekend some parents look as if they have had a 48-hour work-out with the KGB.

When stimulant medication is effective most parents spontaneously say that home life has become 'calmer'. Easing the escalation of bad behaviour and interrogation is what they mean.

What the parents say

'Why can't she put a lid on it?'

'Nothing I do pleases him, whatever he gets, he wants more.'

'We don't tell him when we are going on a trip. If we did he would ask, "Are we going on Wednesday? How will we get there? Are we really going on Wednesday? Are we going by car? Is it Wednesday we are going?"'

'I try to stay calm, but as he goes on and on, my chest feels tight, my neck tenses and I become unbelievably stressed.'

Social clumsiness

Though ADD children are sensitive and caring, frequently they are socially out of tune. They want to be popular with their mates but don't seem to know how to make this happen. They misread the accepted social cues, saying or doing something quite inappropriate. In the group they come on too strong which makes their friends pull away, and wonder 'what sort of a weirdo is this?'

In the playground they want to be part of the main game, but rather than let things take their natural course, they run around, poke, taunt and annoy. The more they try to be friendly, the more they become isolated.

These children function best in the small group setting or with one good friend. Even in this situation they can have problems, being bossy and always needing to be top dog. Friends who come around to play soon leave in a huff.

Social problems hit a peak in primary school and start to ease in high school. In adolescence, however, any remaining insecurities make the normal social uncertainties of this age even greater. When adults bring the remains of their ADD into their grown-up years it is often their social clumsiness they find a particular problem.

What the parents say

'It burns me up, watching him play with his friends. He behaves like an impaired idiot.'

'At school he is known by all, but liked by none.'

'She doesn't have a clue when she is with other people.'

'Other children don't seem to understand him.'

'He's so hurt by being shunned by his schoolmates, though he brings it on himself.'

'He says he has no friends.'

'Before medication he was the only member of the class who was never asked to a birthday party. This year he's been to seven!'

'At times he's quite paranoid. The most innocent things others do are interpreted as deliberate attempts to get at him.'

Poor coordination

Coordination problems come as *fine motor* (colouring, manipulating, handwriting) or *gross motor* (running, climbing, catching a ball, riding a bike).

Most ADD children have difficulty with fine motor tasks, particularly handwriting. The further they get down the page, the greater the untidiness and the more they crossout. Parents and teachers often despair over the quality of this hand work, becoming so obsessed with the writing they fail to spot the talent in the content.

A few ADD children are genuinely clumsy but a larger number appear clumsy due to their poor impulse control. These children charge around like a bull in a china shop, bumping, tripping and spilling as they go. Their knees and elbows are scarred, their lower legs black with bruises.

Many ADD children have a less obvious coordination problem, their difficulty is in planning what they do as well as the quality of their flow of movement. They walk, run and climb efficiently, but it just doesn't look right. They have difficulty coordinating a sequence of movements or doing two things at the one time. At the swimming pool they move their arms and kick their legs, but they don't seem able to breathe in rhythm. At the dance class they love the music but when it comes to formal steps they are lost. Aerobics are impossible as they try to kick, wave, shake and smile all at the one time. Shoelaces are abandoned in favour of velcro.

When children have difficulty throwing and catching a ball, they feel unwelcome in the normal school break-time play activities. A good occupational therapist will never turn this child into an Olympic athlete, but they can improve their performance in the playground. On the positive side many ADD children are superb at sports, and this attribute gives an immense uplift to their self-esteem.

What the parents say

'He's so clumsy, he's last to be picked for any game.'

'I know you tell me her coordination is normal but the way she moves is different from other children.'

'Soccer does not suit, he forgets what he is doing and goes walkabout.'

'If there was one small brick in a big playground, she would trip over it.'

Disorganisation

Many ADD children are highly disorganised. You can see this in their dress: clothes are back to front, inside out and messy, while shoelaces are only half tied. Dirty hands wipe through the hair and over the clothes, and some have 'fiddly fingers', which seem to act without instruction from the brain.

Messages sent from school never get home. The school bag is left on the bus. Swimming costumes are found later at the pool. Books are not brought home to do homework. Many are blind to the trail of mess that surrounds them.

By the early high school years, ADD children are generally tidier but disorganisation is still an impediment. When doing projects, they fiddle, procrastinate and find it hard to get things started. During exams they spend half their time on one question and don't finish the other questions. Many ADD adults acknowledge this vulnerability and protect themselves by living life to a strict, almost obsessive routine.

When an ADD child is disorganised from birth, their messiness will improve with age, and it is important that parents do not to get too worked up along the way. When an obsessively tidy mother produces a completely disorganised child there is the potential for major conflict. Fighting is pointless, as no amount of nagging will change this child in the short term.

What the parents say

'If I ask him to tuck in his shirt, the shirt goes in. As he removes his hand, twice as much comes out.'
'Everything he touches is sticky.'
'He can't see a problem before it hits.'
'When doing homework she lines up her books, takes out a pencil, puts it away, takes out another but can't get started.'
'He's so disorganised, he's the sort of child who could eat a Mars Bar and brush his teeth at the same time.'

Variability

All children and adults have good and bad days, but people with ADD experience extreme variation in performance and mood. These dramatic differences confuse parents, who have often asked if their child might have a double personality or even be schizophrenic!

Parents try to account for the bad days by blaming stress, lack of sleep or some dietary difference. Even when these factors are carefully controlled, the behavioural fluctuations will remain. Their cause is not known, but they are certainly not intentional.

Teachers are particularly aware of this variation. On the occasional good day they are amazed at how so much work can be achieved. On bad days they say that the child might as well have stayed at home. Teachers have to accept that these fluctuations will occur and reward the occasional good day. The bad days have to be accepted as part of ADD and not as a sign of laziness.

What the parents say

'Some days she is so easy to be with. Others she just doesn't know what to be up to.'

'Homework is usually a hassle, then some days he finishes it in 10 minutes.'

'On bad days his teacher sends him to help in the library. She realises he is learning nothing in the classroom.'

'His emotions are all over the place. One minute he's intensely irritating, the next he's devastated at a minor reprimand.'

Poor self-esteem

It is a paradox, but most ADD children are exceptionally sensitive. For this reason it is important to look below all their hustle and hype to see the soft, sensitive centre.

Self-esteem is almost always low in ADD children. Some say it is an inbuilt part of the package of behaviours, others believe it sinks, secondary to failure. These children can put in immense effort at their schoolwork, yet achieve so little. They want to be popular, but they are treated like an annoying outcast. Some achieve well at games, while others are banished to the sideline, as being too 'unco' (uncoordinated) to play with their mates.

This combination of sensitivity, vulnerability and inadequate esteem must be taken seriously. By the age of 20 all the classroom problems will have settled, but any ongoing weakness in socialisation and self-esteem will have implications for the rest of their lives.

What the parents say

'He says he's dumb.'

'She tells me she has no friends'.

'He says he's ugly.'

'No one seems to want to play with him.'

'She now gives up without even trying.'

'He finds it less competitive to hang out with younger children or others with problems.'

Specific learning disabilities

Over half of all children with ADD will have a significant weakness in some academic area. This may be in reading, writing, spelling, language, mathematics or a combination of all of these skills. These problems of learning and language are so frequently associated with ADD that it is important to consider them in every child. It is tough at school when you can't concentrate, organise your work and stick at a task. It is even tougher when there are also unrecognised problems of learning and language (see also Chapter 13).

When is it normal? When is it ADD?

As you have read the list of behaviours covered in this chapter, we can hear you say, 'but these are present in lots of normal children and adults.' That's true, there is no clear cut-off point between the normal child with an active temperament and the one with a mild ADD.

The diagnosis will be made by looking at which behaviours predominate, their magnitude and how well they are being handled. No one is going to set up a behavioural program or give medication unnecessarily. We treat only those whose behaviour and learning is causing problems to themselves and those who care for them.

The difference between the bothersome behaviour of ADD and that of a normal, busy temperament is the trouble it creates. Remember 'A problem is only a problem when it causes a problem.'

Summary: behaviours associated with ADD
Core behaviours

- *Inattention*: The child is easily distracted, forgets instructions, flits from task to task, best with one-to-one supervision.
- *Impulsivity*: The child speaks and acts without thinking and has a short fuse.
- *Overactivity*: The child is restless, fidgety, and has 'rump hyperactivity.'

Additional behaviours

- *Insatiability*: The child is never satisfied, nags, never lets a matter drop.

- *Social clumsiness*: The child is 'out of tune' socially, acts silly in a crowd, misreads social cues.
- *Poor coordination*: The child is clumsy, has poor flow of movement, has difficulty doing two actions at the one time.
- *Disorganisation*: The child is blind to mess, is compelled to touch everything, problems structuring work.
- *Variability*: The child suffers from mood swings, and has good and bad days to the extreme.
- *Specific learning disabilities*: Examples are: dyslexia, language problems, difficulties with mathematics.

5

ADD—Making the Diagnosis

There is no one black and white test for ADD. Anyone who sees the diagnosis in such simple terms has read too many books and worked with far too few children.

If this were an ideal world, each child would have intensive work-outs by psychologists, educators, behaviouralists, occupational therapists, speech pathologists and a paediatrician. But the world we work in has such limited resources we must be economic in assessment and concentrate our energies on providing proper treatment and long-term support.

If parents are concerned with the possibility of ADD, they should first discuss this with the child's teacher. Referral may be made to the school educational psychologist or possibly to a consultant paediatrician or child psychiatrist.

The authors of this book use different methods of assessment, based on their research and practical experience. When Kit Chee assesses she uses formal questionnaires, detailed objective testing and a carefully taken history. Chris Green relies more on the subtleties of history, the presentation of the child and the reports of teachers. We believe that the children and parents in our care are equally well served by either of these approaches. It is the positive response to our intervention that is important, not the individual diagnostic method.

Diagnosis—the four steps

We see the diagnosis of ADD as being comprised of four simple steps:

1. Look for alarm signals.
2. Exclude ADD lookalikes.
3. Use some objective pointers towards diagnosis.
4. Take a detailed history tuned to the subtleties of ADD.

Alarm signals

There are two main alarm signals that should always make one think of ADD:

1. *When a child significantly underfunctions at school, despite having a normal intellect and no major specific learning disabilities.*

2. *When a child has a specific package of behaviour problems which are considerably worse than would be expected for the standard of parenting and home environment.*

Underfunctions at school

Most parents of ADD children seek our help after the start of school. The teacher is bewildered as this child appears clever but is unable to deliver the goods. The school may arrange for an educational psychologist to test overall intellect and to exclude specific learning disabilities. The results show a degree of failure which is not in keeping with the intellect and specific learning abilities. ADD must now be considered as a possibility.

Unexpected behaviour problems

At home the children in this family have equal love and discipline, yet this one child stands out as many times more difficult. The parents will be making heavy weather of management, due to a cluster of telltale ADD behaviours.

Once alerted to the possibility of ADD, it is time to move to the next step.

Exclude ADD lookalikes

Many academic articles imply that ADD is easily confused with a long list of lookalike behaviours. This may be true on paper, but in practice an experienced observer will quickly cut through any confusion. The most commonly quoted list includes the normal active preschooler; the hearing impaired child; intellectual disability; specific learning disabilities; autism; brain injury; epilepsy; childhood depression; family dysfunction. (For a full list of ADD lookalikes, see Appendix XI.)

Pointers towards diagnosis

Over the years researchers have worked hard to bring some science to the diagnosis of ADD. Questionnaires have been

created which allow teachers and parents to rate the behaviours. The American Psychiatric Association has come up
with a list of diagnostic criteria. Psychologists have developed
tests and profiles that point to the presence of ADD. Others
have devised ways to measure attention and persistence. Recently, advanced electronics have allowed the analysis of
brainwaves which some believe to be helpful (neurometrics).

Professionals may promote their way of assessing as the one
and only method, but there remains no completely reliable test
for ADD. The methods currently available bring some objectivity into a very subjective area, but they are not foolproof and
can be seen as nothing more than pointers towards a probable
diagnosis of ADD.

Questionnaires

Parents and teachers can complete questionnaires which score
specific ADD behaviours—the higher the score, the more likelihood of ADD. Among those most commonly used are the
Conners Teacher and Parent Rating Scales, the Achenbach
Child Behaviour Checklists, the Edelbrock Child Attention
Problems Rating Scale and the Barkley and DuPaul ADHD
Rating Scale. These questionnaires allow for some objectivity,
both in making the diagnosis and monitoring the effects of
treatment. (See Appendixes IV and V.)

The American Psychiatric Association diagnostic criteria (DSM-IV)

The DSM–IV (1994) guidelines give reasonably clear criteria
for the diagnosis of ADD. It is classified into three main types:

1. Attention Deficit Hyperactivity Disorder—with predominantly hyperactive–impulsive type behaviour (fidgety, restless, impulsive, impatient).

2. Attention Deficit Hyperactivity Disorder—with predominantly inattentive behaviour (dreamy, non-listening, easily distracted, inattentive, subtle learning problems).

3. Attention Deficit Hyperactivity Disorder—combined type—probably the most common presentation (inattentive and hyperactive, impulsive behaviour (see Appendix I for list of criteria)).

Psychometric tests and profiles

Each child believed to have ADD should be given a standard intelligence test, followed by specialised assessments in reading, writing, spelling, maths and language. Unfortunately, as there are such limited resources, for most this remains an ideal, but not a reality.

During testing, the psychologist may comment that the child is restless, inattentive and hard to keep working at a task. But this is not always the case; some children with major ADD can hold their concentration in this quiet one-to-one environment, but are unable to do so in a noisy classroom.

When a standard intelligence test is given it ensures that general intellectual slowness is not the cause of the poor behaviour and underachievement. The testing procedure used by most psychologists is made up of many subtests and ADD children often produce a broad range of subscores. They are particularly weak in tasks that require sequencing ability and short-term memory.

When these subtests are analysed, psychologists come up with the Kaufman factors, one of which reflects the child's freedom from distractibility. This is said to indicate the presence of

ADD, but we and many others see it as overrated and unreliable in diagnosis.

A new breed of psychologists, the neuropsychologists, look at more specialised functions of learning, in particular frontal lobe function. This part of the brain, which influences sense and the control of basic impulses, is often weak in people with ADD. Neuropsychology can help pinpoint these problems, but at present it is more of academic interest than a precise pointer to ADD. (See Appendixes IX and X for description of WISC–III, Kaufman factor and Neuropsychology tests).

Tests of attention and persistence

These tests measure the main areas of weakness with ADD (attention and persistence). They help make the diagnosis and then quantify the response to medication. These are probably some of the most useful tests available but they are still not foolproof.

The Paired Associate Learning Test.
Here the psychologist verbally teaches a task, continually monitoring and scoring how well the information has been retained. This is a simple test of attention and memory, which requires no computer technology and is said to have reasonable accuracy (see detailed description Appendix IX).

Continuous Performance Test.
This is a computer driven test which requires the child to respond when an image appears on a screen. This has been well standardised and formally measures impulsivity and distractibility (see detailed description in Appendix IX).

Neurometrics, Brain Electrical Activity Mapping (BEAM) and specialised brainwave tests

These techniques involve computer analysis of brainwave tracings, which can differentiate between ADD, ADD with associated specific learning disability and the normal child. The tracings may also change when there is a response to medication. This concept sounds exciting, but at present it is still viewed by most as nothing more than another pointer (for details see Appendix VII).

History and observation

After seeing many ADD children it becomes apparent that no two are exactly the same. Despite this, if one takes a careful history which is tuned to ADD, there are usually telltale signs.

Frequent findings with ADD children

- About one-third will have been normal infants who became toddler tornadoes, the moment they got up on their feet.
- At preschool about half stood out in their inability to sit and settle at story time. Some upset other children.
- For many ADD children, the first school report used the words, 'disruptive', 'distractible', 'goes walkabout'.
- There is a dramatic difference between academic achievement in the one-to-one situation versus unsupervised study.
- Most are restless, and as you talk to them they fidget and their eyes flit.
- At home most ADD children are insatiable (can't put a lid on it) and have an uncanny knack of generating tension.

- Their behaviour in a group is often embarrassing and when playing with one other child they are overpowering and bossy.

- Their impulsivity makes them both verbally and physically accident-prone.

- As you talk to the parents you quickly sense their frustration, stress and confusion. (This is different to the feeling you get from the parents of a defiant, poorly managed child.)

- In the office young, impulsive, overactive children are easy to diagnose. The moment they walk in the door, the doctor will by reflex reach out to protect their property.

- In the office older children present less dramatically. Most squirm, fidget and fiddle. Their talk often gets side-tracked or they become lost in mid-sentence. Asking questions often gets the answer, 'Good.' Their eyes and minds are all over the place.

- We estimate that over 90 per cent of ADD children can be identified as such by a properly tuned history. Sometimes ADD will not be obvious in the doctor's office and then the diagnosis is made by listening carefully to the parents. When this happens, ADD is diagnosed in the same way as many other medical conditions, for example, epilepsy; that is, by history. Doctors don't ask to see the epileptic fall to the floor and fit in front of them, they believe what parents tell them.

Those who present with pure inattention and subtle problems of learning are much more difficult to diagnose, and with them the tests and pointers are of special value. When major family dysfunction and the heavy behaviours of Oppositional Defiant Disorder or Conduct Disorder cloud the picture, diagnosis may become exceptionally difficult. With experience it gets easier, but it is never straightforward.

Conclusion

Sometimes too much science makes a simple job complicated. For instance, if our task was to tell the difference between a wild wolf and a friendly German Shepherd, we could create a series of objective checklists, tests and measurements. But even without these, few of us would be confused if one ran at us. As in most parts of medicine, the eye of the experienced beholder is more important than a laboratory load of tests.

With limited resources we must not fall into the trap of over-diagnosis and undertreatment. Diagnosis is only the start; it is what happens after that which really matters.

Summary: making the diagnosis

As we hear some colleagues talk on ADD and Specific Learning Disabilities (SLD) it seems that the diagnosis is impossible without a team of psychologists and a month of time. Resources are so limited at present, anyone who teaches about ADD must be clear as to what are the essentials to diagnosis and what are the impractical academic ideals.

With this in mind we put forward our three plans for assessment: the basic, the more objective and the comprehensive.

1 The basic method

Be alerted

- Behaviour out of step with parenting (fidgets, impulsive, insatiable, socially out of tune)
- Underfunctions at school (disruptive, distractible, inattentive, needs one-to-one supervision)

Exclude

- Obvious intellectual retardation
- Major family dysfunction

Talk to school

- Is there any worry re intelligence?
- Is there any worry re SLD?
- What are the school's concerns?

Appointment with

- Psychologist, paediatrician or child psychiatrist
- Diagnosis made having considered the above and then confirmed by parents' description and clinical presentation in the consulting room

Trial of stimulants
Monitored by:

- Feedback from school
- Feedback from parents

2 The more objective method

Be alerted

- Behaviour out of step with parenting (fidgets, impulsive, insatiable, socially out of tune)
- Underfunctions at school (disruptive, distractible, inattentive, needs one-to-one supervision)

Exclude

- Obvious intellectual retardation
- Major family dysfunction

Talk to school

- Is there any worry re intelligence?
- Is there any worry re SLD?
- What are the school's concerns?

Paperwork
- Questionnaires completed by parents
- Questionnaires completed by school
- Formal report from school/preschool

Educational psychologist
- Basic tests of intellect
- Screening tests for SLD
- Classroom visit to observe

Appointment with
- Psychologist, paediatrician or child psychiatrist.
- Diagnosis made having considered the above and then confirmed by parents' description and clinical presentation in the consulting room

Trial of stimulants
Monitored by:
- Feedback from school
- Feedback from parents
- Repeat questionnaires

3 The more comprehensive method

Be alerted
- Behaviour out of step with parenting (fidgets, impulsive, insatiable, socially out of tune)
- Underfunctions at school (disruptive, distractible, inattentive, needs one-to-one supervision)

Exclude
- Obvious intellectual retardation
- Major family dysfunction

Talk to school

- Is there any worry re intelligence?
- Is there any worry re SLD?
- What are the school's concerns?

Paperwork

- Questionnaires completed by parents
- Questionnaires completed by school
- Formal report from school/preschool

Specialised tests

- Educational psychologist: detailed tests of general abilities and specific areas of learning
- Educationalist: practical assessment of basic abilities in classroom learning
- Paediatrician–Psychologist: Paired Associate Learning Test; Continuous Performance Type Test; Neurometrics

Appointment with

- Psychologist, paediatrician or child psychiatrist.
- Diagnosis made having considered the above and then confirmed by parents' description and clinical presentation in the consulting room

Trial of stimulants

Monitored by some of the following:

- Questionnaires
- Paired Associate Learning Test
- Neurometrics
- Continuous performance test
- Feedback from school
- Feedback from parents

PART 2

Help For Parents, Teachers and Children

6

Navigating Through the ADD Minefield

By the time families see medical professionals, many have had a real run around. Often they have been told, 'There's nothing wrong,' 'It's poor parenting,' 'You need to be stricter,' 'It's all in the diet,' 'You didn't bond to your baby,' 'Maternal depression,' 'Marriage stress,' 'Problems of perception,' 'Visual difficulties,' 'Laziness' or 'General lack of ability.'

Parents and ADD children

Parents are particularly disadvantaged when professionals are quick to give an opinion on ADD, but slow to stay up-to-date with the modern literature. They feel angry when experts rubbish other experts, yet have little to offer themselves. They are confused when schools encourage some ill-proven therapy, while making the parents feel guilty if they opt for a properly researched treatment (such as stimulant medication).

It never ceases to amaze us just how many experts may have seen a child, before the correct diagnosis is made. Recently, we saw an eight-year-old with classic ADD but the diagnosis had never been made. Over the previous two years the parents had sought help from two educational psychologists, a private psychologist, an occupational therapist, a paediatrician and two different child psychiatrists. An impressive list of diagnoses had been made, but none of them included ADD. As this busy boy walked into our waiting room, an elderly grandmother looked up and said, 'He's got ADD just like my grandson.' She was right. Often an insightful parent can see much more clearly than a college full of professionals.

Once a diagnosis of ADD is made this can stir up all sorts of mixed emotions.

Guilt

If you have an ADD child, even the most knowledgable, best balanced parent secretly believes that they are in some way to blame. This feeling can be made worse by out-of-date community attitudes which often see ADD as a parent problem.

Then there are those interfering people who question the diagnosis and tell the parents that the treatment is not safe. It upsets us to see good mums and dads blame themselves, when we know that their children were 'born difficult', and would be many times worse, if it weren't for their excellent parents.

Disappointment and anger

By the time we see families many parents have done their best, but nothing they try seems to work and they now feel impotent and inadequate. Many are disappointed that parenthood has not lived up to expectation. Others are angry that one child has brought so much stress and disruption to what was once a hassle-free household.

Some mothers have a supportive, heavily involved husband, others are left with all the worry and childcare. Many mothers we meet now find themselves sole parents, often looking after the difficult children of difficult men. No one says it is fair, and there are no simple answers.

Dads better than mums

Mothers may provide the consistency in childcare and be responsible for 90 per cent of the parenting, but ADD children still behave better for their fathers. This normal imbalance is unfair and erodes the confidence of many mums. It is not that mothers are poor parents, it is just that fathers tend to be firmer, louder and less well known by their children.

Parents who can't be helped

There is another side to this—some parents refuse to accept the nature of ADD. As we talk they won't listen, they won't change and can't be helped.

Treat all equal: Some parents are quite angry when we suggest they treat the ADD child in a different way to their siblings: 'He's not going to change our life,' 'You can't tell us that one child should be treated differently,' 'If they're going to live in our house they will live by the same rules.' With this attitude they make no allowance for ADD, the child protests, home becomes unhappy and the continual criticism erodes all esteem.

Looking for trouble: A country mother recently complained that the trip home from school was a time of great tension: 'I stop to get the groceries, when I return to the car he has his brothers and sisters at each others' throats.' We suggested that she do the shopping on the way to pick up the children, but this minor change didn't suit.

Another mother complained of problems when she picked up her six-year-old after school. 'He runs out, jumps around, gets into the car, climbs over the seats, toots the horn, and then we get into an impossible argument.' We suggested she drove off as soon as this sparky child was released from school. 'Are you telling me that I don't have the right to talk to my friends, for as long as I wish? I am not going to be dictated to by a six-year-old.'

Beat it out of them: If the child had an obvious disability, it would be easier to accept. If deaf, we accept that no amount of shouting or beating would make them hear. ADD is also a physical condition but some parents refuse to accept this fact, then push, punish and get nowhere.

Fathers are often just as uninsightful, inflexible and impulsive as the child they produced. Some are quite immovable, 'I would never have been allowed to get away with this when I was a boy.' This unproductive approach continues and frequently we see these children years later, with major reactive behaviours. They are telling the parents they got it wrong, but by now it is too late.

Summary: the ADD minefield

As parents struggle with the day-to-day dramas of ADD, emotions run high. Even the world's best parents feel inadequate, guilty, disappointed or downright angry.

It is as if they are standing in a minefield. In this explosive situation there are only three ways to go:

1. You can stand still, protest and demand that someone digs up the mines and removes the problem. No matter how much you complain the mines will still remain.

2. The next option is to stamp on unperturbed. You make no allowances, treat all the children the same and try to beat the ADD child into shape. You can follow this course, but the stress it generates will blow your family apart.

3. Finally, you can accept the situation as it is and take a course that steps round the biggest bangs. We (the authors) are peace lovers, you know what path we hope you will choose.

Helping Home Behaviours

We suggest seven steps to better behaviour. These will never turn a Rambo into a quiet social saint, but they can help parents move from enduring, back to enjoying.

The seven steps

1. Accept your child as is.
2. Pursue the peaceful path.
3. Implement routine.

4. Communicate clearly.
5. Spot the triggers and detonators.
6. Be positive—boost the good.
7. Set up safety valves for the big blow-ups.

Accept your child as is

ADD is part of the child's make-up and many of the behavioural outbursts are largely outside their control. This is a physical problem, such as bad asthma. If your child was wheezing and breathless you wouldn't say it was all in their mind, neither would you blame them when they ran slower than their friends.

ADD is very real, and you had better accept it, because no amount of parental aggro will ever make them behave perfectly. They are different from their brothers, sisters, cousins and schoolmates. You don't let them get away with murder, but special allowances must be made.

The peaceful path

Children with ADD generate immense stress in their families, yet stress is the number one catalyst that sets off bad behaviour. It seems a soft suggestion, to tell parents to stand smiling as their child numbs their nerves. The truth is, whether it is easy or not, calm creates the environment which is most conducive to keeping relationships close and children under control.

Parents must put the filters up in front of their eyes, focus on the few big behaviours that matter and not rise to the rest. As we point this out to parents, you can see them smile. They accept what we say holds great wisdom but they know we don't have to live with their child.

Implement routine

An ADD child must be sure of where they stand; they can't cope when the ground rules keep changing. They need routine, structure and to know what is going to happen next. These disorganised children like to feel there is a framework which directs their day. They wake at a certain time, put their pyjamas under their pillow, straighten the duvet, get dressed, have breakfast, brush their teeth and leave for school. If their equilibrium is thrown by anything unexpected—a late night, a relief teacher, unannounced visitors or a trip away from home—this will set them off. If you want peace, then stick to the plan.

Communicate clearly

Children who are inattentive, impulsive and apparently deaf to discipline, need the clearest communication and instruction. First, gain good eye contact using warm but decisive words. State simply what you want and give instructions, clearly, step by step. Mumbling, nagging, debating, shouting and talking over the television will get you nowhere.

Triggers and detonators

Parents know that certain things are dynamite to discipline, but still they stumble into them every time. After a while you know what's going to cause the trouble—long telephone calls, visits to boring friends, children's parties, car journeys, arguments. Some parents tramp on unperturbed, but most use their brains and steer clear of trouble spots.

Be positive—boost the good

Good behavioural technique tells us to acknowledge and reinforce good behaviour, while the bad is underplayed and hopefully extinguished. Every parent knows this theory, but after a difficult day we soon slip into the role of the negative nagger. The moment this happens everyone becomes tense, the behaviour escalates, relationships are stressed and often you wonder if contraception might have been a better course.

The aim is to be a positive parent. Note, boost and reward the good. Use praise, attention, privileges, tokens or even things that smack of bribery. When behaviour is not good, try to ignore the trivia and, when necessary, give a clear, short warning then act decisively.

Safety valves—time-out

There comes a point in managing the ADD child, where parents see things are rapidly escalating out of control. Once behaviour gets past this point, there ceases to be any place for reason or rational thinking. Now is the time to back off and put in place a safety valve.

Time-out is one such technique where a deteriorating situation can be salvaged by briefly removing the child from all attention and audience. Some suggest a quiet corner or a 'time-out' chair, while we favour a period of isolation in the bedroom. There the child remains for approximately one minute for every year of life. Only when quiet, even though not openly repentant, may they return to the real world.

Some parents issue a warning, then remove a mark from a token system. Be careful—once the situation becomes heated, this may backfire with the child throwing a major tantrum, just to get their money's worth.

When behaviour gets totally out of control, some parents just cut their losses and get out of earshot. There is no one safety valve that suits every child at every age, but if you find one that works, use it.

Particular problems

Siblings and competition

Most ADD children behave reasonably well when out alone with their parents. Put them in the company of their brothers and sisters, however, and soon you are sitting in a war zone. Forget fairness, life will be more peaceful if special allowances are made for the ADD child. When fights start, divert or ignore but don't get caught up in the conflict. Stay out of it, brothers and sisters will usually reach their own equilibrium.

All children can get a fair deal if care is shared for part of the time. At the weekend one parent should give some undivided attention to the ADD child, while brothers and sisters have fun with the other parent.

Choices

The young, immature, insatiable ADD child does not cope well with choices. The more you offer, the greater becomes their discontent. If you want them to go somewhere, just go—actions speak louder than words.

Visits and parties

ADD children are wound up by children's parties and often find adult events boring. Be selective in any invitation you accept; socialisation comes with maturity, it is not something that should be forced. If parties are a hassle, aim for a short, sharp visit, and leave while the child's behaviour is still accept-able. If children come to adult outings remember that they also have rights, they need some of your time.

Children cause poor parenting

Parents start out with high ideals, but after years of getting no-where, we become more resigned to the situation, back off and underdiscipline. A passing professional comes along and blames all the bad behaviour on this lack of firmness. Discipline often appears poor but this can be due to the degree of diffi-culty faced by the parents.

This fact was demonstrated nicely by a group of researchers using video recordings to analyse the interaction between ADD children and their parents. As the videos were analysed these parents did not rate well in their discipline of the children. They were much more negative, snappy, stressed and inappro-priate in their responses than parents of non-ADD children. On face value it was this poor parenting that was causing the ADD child to behave badly.

Then the children were given their stimulant medication. When the families were refilmed, the same parents were found to be calm, controlled and disciplining well. The parents were the same, it was the children who had changed.

Many doctors, psychologists, teachers and relatives have not yet recognised this fact. *It is often the behaviour of an ADD child that creates the problems of discipline, not the problems of discipline that create the behaviour.*

Summary: helping home behaviours

- Have realistic expectations.
- Make allowances.
- Implement routine and consistency.

- In the behavioural minefield, steer round the mines.
- Don't rise to unimportant irritation.
- Keep calm, don't escalate.
- Act, don't debate.
- Give rapid, repeated rewards.
- Don't get demoralised. Every parent finds ADD discipline difficult.

8

Structuring School for Success

Trying to teach a restless, inattentive child is never easy. Even with the best of intentions many problems will remain, because ADD is a chronic condition. There are no simple solutions, teachers must not despair but fortify themselves for the long haul.

Which class?

The ADD child thrives on calm, consistency and structure. If they were royalty, they would have a full-time personal tutor, but in the real world they will be taught in the same room as 30 others. When choosing a class, aim for the traditional closed plan style, avoiding the composites, where more than one year's grade is taught together, unless there is some exceptional draw-card, such as a high teacher to pupil ratio.

ADD children do not cope well with unexpected surprises. They need to know what is planned at the start of every day. Clear guidelines are essential and there must be no doubt as to the consequences when these are not met. The rules should be outlined in a way that is warm but positive, and 100 per cent convincing. Consistency is all important but so is the insight to know when to back off when things are escalating out of hand. The ADD child is at their most vulnerable when moving from one situation to another, so they need time to settle after an excursion or play period.

ADD children cannot cope with change, so keep them away from teachers with an unreliable attendance record and those who are about to go on long service leave. In small schools, these children are often incorrectly placed in a class taken by the school principal. He or she may be the most tolerant and experienced teacher in the school, but the ADD child is unsettled by all the administrative interruptions that go with the job.

Some teachers don't suit

For the ADD child, success at school varies greatly from year to year. It is not so much that the children change, it is just that some years the pupil and teacher hit it off and some years they don't.

A number of teachers believe that the ADD child can be sorted out with some heavy discipline. Others are almost as impulsive and inflexible as the ADD child, which leads to blow-ups in behaviour.

The choice of teacher is all important; when there are chemistry clashes between teacher and child, the classroom is not a happy place. These children need a teacher who is insightful, predictable, organised and encouraging. They need to know that they are accepted and appreciated but at the same time that the teacher is firmly in charge.

Increasing tuned-in time

When a child is inattentive, cannot persist at tasks and easily bored, the first teaching task is to increase the period for which the child is tuned-in to the teacher. The following points are suggestions to help in this regard.

Sensible seating

It is tempting for a teacher to hide the disruptive child as far away from the rest of the class as possible. But if they are going to learn the child needs to be in the front third of the class and kept well away from distracting influences. Select the two most placid pupils and sandwich the ADD child between them, to be sedated by their soothing aura.

Communication and cues

ADD children will never learn if we don't help them to listen. Instructions must appear to be individual, yet not make them stand out from their mates in the classroom.

If teaching is presented in a bored, unexcited voice it is unlikely to get past the left ear lobe. The first step in communication is to gain attention and eye contact using an enthusiastic, firm, businesslike tone. When the class is drifting, the clever teacher uses cue words, such as 'Ready,' 'Wait for it,' 'This is the interesting bit,' 'Now, here we go!'

Step-wise instruction

Long lists of instructions do not suit the ADD child. Their memory lapses, they forget the order of the instructions and the result is a shambles. In the primary school years, difficult work needs to be taught in a series of simple steps. As they get older, children can teach themselves to break down a task and by the teenage years they will be talking themselves through a sequence of instructions, just as a pilot runs through a checklist prior to take-off. This self-imposed order is the key to success in high school and in exams. ADD children need to plan everything with headings and lists, and within a structure. If they don't, they ramble off and miss the main messages.

Active teaching

ADD children often sit smiling while their teacher's words drift over their heads. If teaching is going to work there must be plenty of active participation. Questions can be asked, or the child can be asked to play teacher and teach the lesson back to the class.

Pictures, diagrams, outlines and models all give variety and help to reinforce listening. Inattentive children have a poor short-term memory, and they need to be able to go over something again when bits are missed. They can be helped by notes, regular revision and encouraging them to ask questions.

Ask when they need help

In years gone by teachers may have been seen as stern, unapproachable people, but this is not the case today. From the earliest days at school all children must be encouraged to speak up when they don't understand. Teachers find that half a minute of time when the question occurs can prevent weeks being wasted in the future. Asking is important if children are to avoid the demoralisation that comes with dropping behind in their work.

Communication with home

Messages about homework, outings and special events rarely seem to make it home. It is frustrating, but no amount of chiding will reorganise the ADD child overnight. When important information needs to get to parents, teachers should write a note and stick it somewhere where it will be found, such as the lid of the lunch-box.

When behaviour programs are put in place (see Chapters 7 and 9) a communication book between school and home, which should be written in by both teacher and parents, helps to reinforce the results. Report cards also give an update on behaviour and school work. They are useful if not burnt, buried or lost on the way home.

By high school the adolescent who wants to achieve will realise the importance of organisation, writing in a diary and making a 'to do' list for each day. Even in the technologically advanced nineties the old-fashioned memory jogs of knots in handkerchiefs and marks on hands still have their place, as do reminder rhymes, such as 'i before e, except after c'.

Homework

This is mostly the school's problem and must never be allowed to ruin family relationships. Once released from school busy children feel that they have done more than their fair share of sitting and studying. They need time to unwind, eat and blast off some energy.

Each night homework should start at the same time and be done on a strict contract basis. A quarter or half hour of full-on attention is expected, then rewarded by walkabout or a snack, then a prompt return to the work. Procrastination, diversions and fiddling around are not accepted. These short bursts of effort can be timed with a kitchen timer. Reward the effort, not the amount of work completed.

Doing homework with an ADD child can be an amazingly frustrating experience. One childcare author recently told us 'I've given up trying to help with homework. It was only a matter of time before I'd be in the child abuse courts and that would be bad for book sales.'

Remedial help

With ADD so intertwined with specific learning disabilities, many of these children will need extra help with reading, writing, mathematics and language. In an ideal world the school system would be adequately funded to provide small classes and the required remedial workers. Unfortunately, times are tough and parents need to push hard for any extra help they can get. Small classes are few and far between and most support for these children comes through the personal efforts of perceptive principals and class teachers.

Parents pay for private tutors, who are often of great value, but too much out of school tutoring can become a turn-off to learning. ADD children find their school day tough enough without returning home to have their noses wiped in further failure. It is unhealthy to spend so much time focusing on areas of weakness; outside interests are also important.

Exam technique

By the high school years many ADD children have developed the drive and determination to really succeed. With organisation they learn to study, using lists, memory jogs, highlighter pens and frequent revision. Despite these learning aids most will underperform in their exams. Questions are misread, time is allocated unwisely, and they are disadvantaged by poor writing and unreliable spelling.

Schools are often surprised at the amount of hidden talent when they test the ADD child by oral exam or allow a scribe to do their writing. When approaching major exams it is not enough for these children to master the course, they also have to learn the most effective way of getting the information down on paper. Examination boards will permit some candidates to use a scribe and in future ADD pupils may do much of their work on a laptop computer, with a spell-check facility.

Repeating years

Most ADD children underfunction socially and emotionally to about two-thirds of their actual age. At school their learning may be up to standard level but they are out of their depth emotionally.

As a child's brain matures many of their problems with attention, behaviour and learning get easier. For this reason it is better to take school at a somewhat slower pace.

Some experts worry about the child's esteem if held back behind their age group, but we take a different view. We believe there are great benefits to both esteem and learning, if held back when educationally and emotionally out of one's depth.

Summary: success at school

- A firm, flexible, encouraging teacher.
- Seat near the front of the class, away from distraction.
- Communicate with enthusiasm, clarity and cue words.
- Instruct in short, simple steps.

- Give brief bursts of full-on learning followed by rest/reward.
- Allow the opportunity to replay and revise (written notes, teach again, tutoring).
- Encourage child to ask when they don't understand.
- Use memory jogs, for example: 'i before e, except after c'.
- Encourage self-monitoring, find your own mistakes, talk through each step.
- Focus on structure, headings, planning and seeing the salient points.
- Homework on a strict contract basis. Reward effort.
- Encourage self-esteem by giving responsibility, privileges and showing interest.
- *Help*, don't *humiliate*.

9

Better Management of School Behaviours

Never let a behavioural expert tell you that managing an impulsive, insatiable, immature child is easy. You can put in place the best behaviour modification plan, but it will never work the way they tell you in the training manual. Most of these children don't plan to be badly behaved, it just seems to happen. They do, however, respond well to encouragement, and anything that arouses their interest and boosts their esteem. They also need firm limits and routine, as well as rewards that are given quickly and often.

Keeping the peace

As mentioned many times in this book, ADD children are extremely sensitive to activity around them and tension in the air. Unimportant irritations must pass without comment. Teachers need to keep calm, and even when driven close to the edge, they must hang on tight to their self-control.

Reward to reinforce

The theory of behaviour modification therapy states that when a good behaviour is rewarded (reinforced) it is likely to be repeated. Where an undesirable behaviour is underplayed (extinguished) it will probably not happen again. Rewards can either be 'soft rewards', as in giving attention, or 'hard rewards', such as handing out stamps, tokens and privileges.

In the younger ADD child, behaviour modification will only work if rewards are immediate, impressive and frequent. If the child has behaved well from the before school assembly to mid-morning break, reward them at that time, not the end of the day. When work is done well acknowledge this, and possibly choose them to take a special message or allow them time on the computer.

Attention is usually the most valuable reward, but with 30 children in a class the ADD child wants more than their share so they will attempt to hijack their teacher's attention with some irritating act. They taunt, act smart and make animal noises, but don't blow a gasket—remember that any behaviour that is emphasised, either good or bad, will be repeated.

Time-out

When psychologists talk of 'time out' this means 'time out from positive reinforcement'. The aim is to remove the child from a negative, no win situation and cut them off from all positive attention. You can put them on a chair in a quiet corner or in a peaceful place outside the room. Time-out is not supposed to be a painful punishment, it is a means of extracting the child from an unproductive interaction. This allows both parties time to cool down.

Token systems

With the ADD child's great need for regular reinforcement, sometimes we suggest a token reward system. This system rewards the child with a couple of counters, ticks on their work or poker chips every time something remarkable happens, or perhaps after every trouble free half hour. Tokens can also be forfeited when there is disruption, disturbance to others or a refusal to keep to the rules.

The aim is to collect sufficient tokens to trade in for some special privilege. For the reasonably behaved, these can be given at the end of the day or chalked up against a greater treat when the week has finished. The ADD child mightn't be able to wait that long, and the rewards may have to be more immediate.

One word of warning: this system must be aimed at giving, not taking away, tokens. Once the impulsive child starts to see their store of tokens slip away they may go for broke. Many parents have found this out to their great cost. After some minor incident the child sees that they will not get their special treat so they retaliate with the most unbelievably bad behaviour.

Know when to cut your losses

Every teacher knows there will be days when educating the impulsive, inattentive child is impossible. When learning and behaviour slip into that downward spiral it is time to pursue peace, not education.

Don't fight it—get them out for a while, send them on a message or to work in the library. Maybe even suggest that they go and help the principal's secretary—after all, a problem shared is a problem halved!

Playground behaviour

Many ADD children are impulsive, 'over the top' and upset others in the playground. It is not that they are aggressive or deliberately naughty, they just don't know how to behave in a group.

No matter how we counsel these children, when teased they continue to rise to the bait. The ADD child is an easy target, hunted out by those who have a chip on their shoulder and need someone to taunt. When teachers complain about these blow-ups, it is important to look past the child's response and see who was guilty of upsetting them in the first place.

Many ADD children are easily led, and while those who influence them back off, they are left to carry the blame. Over the years we have seen numerous school bags land on the roof, fire extinguishers released and rude messages delivered to other pupils.

When the ADD child is in trouble every lunch hour, and the above behaviour modification strategies have been unsuccessful, it is time to call in a force of United Nations peacekeepers, or think about some stimulant medication. As the former seem a bit busy at present, go for the stimulants, they have helped many children to play peacefully and become better accepted.

Summary: better behaviour at school

- Let them know the day's program and stick to it.
- Ignore trivial, unimportant irritations.
- Be on guard at times of change (for example, coming in from play).
- Reward good behaviour; don't get it back to front.
- Avoid escalation; know when to back off.
- Use 'time out' and token systems.
- When the taunts of other children get the ADD child into trouble, punish the real culprit.
- Teaching may be tough but remember, at 3.30 pm, it will be someone else's problem!

10

Other Therapies and Diet

The last 15 years has been an interesting time. First, we heard that ADD would disappear when lead was removed from petrol. Then we digressed into diet, vitamin B6, zinc and, more recently, multivitamins. Tinted lenses and eye exercises were promoted for dyslexia. Sensory integration therapy was said to help the learning disabled, motor programs came and went.

Psychiatrists tried to understand the thinking of ADD children through play, while their parents often found their emotions examined in long-term talking therapy. Along the way there have been a number of psychological treatments that were sound in theory but decidedly disappointing in their results.

Meanwhile, the media has feasted on far-fetched, often wacky claims, and professionals with a particular axe to grind have often rubbished those with a more up-to-date overview. It is no wonder that parents are confused.

Let's look at some of these much promoted forms of therapy. Which of these help in theory, which help in practice, and which don't help at all?

Cognitive behaviour therapy

In this technique the psychologist gets a child to talk their way through what is happening around them, and then to be more reasoned and reflective in the way they respond to a situation. The hope is that the cognitively trained child will then teach themselves to step back a pace, and self-regulate their own behaviour. This seems a sensible form of treatment for every child with ADD, but unfortunately the results have been very disappointing.

The young ADD child is far too impulsive to think through a situation before they react. In older children the results are better but not great.

Social skills training

ADD children appear unaware of how their behaviour bothers other people. They are greatly disadvantaged by being socially out of tune, and when the technique of social skills training arrived, we saw this as an exciting innovation.

In this program, children are taught in groups to think how their words and behaviours affect those around them. If they interact well this good behaviour is reinforced; when they behave badly they are asked to reflect on how this affects others.

Social skills training seems essential for every child with ADD but, unfortunately, the results have been far from good. Research shows that social skills can be taught in the therapy room but the benefits have little flow on to the outside world.

Sensory integration

In the early 1970s, an American therapist, Jean Ayres, popularised the idea of sensory integration. Her main interest was the learning disabilities which are often part of ADD. Her techniques involve the child in movement, swinging, spinning and attaining balance. These actions were thought to help brain maturation, which has a flow on to academic and other abilities.

There are still a number of international centres which promote variations of Ayres' work, but we do not recommend these theories to patients in our care. We have not been impressed with the results we have seen and recent studies show the therapeutic effect of sensory integration has no advantage over those of the more simple traditional interventions. (see Appendix XVIII: Controversial therapies for ADD).

Occupational therapy

Most ADD children have terrible handwriting. This can be helped by a good occupational therapist, who will work on the pen grip, organisation of the letters and the flow from word to word. Stimulant medication is often used in conjunction with occupational therapy as this also helps with both neatness and accuracy.

Many ADD children have poor motor planning and coordination, which leaves them unable to tie shoelaces, throw straight, catch a ball or to move smoothly. A short period with an enthusiastic therapist can help a child to make the best of what they have got and at the same time give a great boost to self-confidence. Occupational therapy can bring about a percentage improvement, but it will never turn the child with two left feet into a world class athlete or graceful dancer (see also Appendixes XVI and XVII).

The talking cures

The current attitudes in the UK are reminiscent of those in Australia in the 1980s, during which the majority of private child psychiatrists were more interested in the environmental–analytical, rather than the biological–behavioural approach. Many believed that ADD behaviours came from unresolved feelings, dysfunctions and past events in the parent's lives. Often parents were taken into long-term therapy, to talk through their perceived problems, while some children were engaged through play.

These ideas were 20 years behind the more pragmatic, eclectic views of our North American colleagues. These entrenched Australian attitudes were challenged by some medical professionals, such as the late Dr Gordon Serfontein, who saw ADD as an inherited, biological problem which was not caused by poor parenting.

There was an uncomfortable period in the mid 1980s where Serfontein and others were accused of colluding with parents to prevent them from facing up to their role in causing the condition. There was even greater uproar when these 'parent problems' were treated with stimulant medication.

Influential psychiatrists and psychologists who continue to be uncomfortable with our views—that parents are not to blame and ADD is a result of a brain dysfunction—are a shrinking minority. Most modern-minded child psychiatrists see play therapy, with an inattentive, unthinking child, to be of little value. Certainly the 'talking cures' have a place in managing the emotional problems of some parents, but not in treating ADD. Formal family therapy is generally unhelpful, though clever psychiatrists use a less structured approach to help all members of a family work together to support their ADD sibling.

Psychiatrists and psychologists have a major role to play in dealing with ADD children. This is in making the diagnosis, implementing behavioural programs and supporting parents.

Developmental optometry—eye exercises

When vision and eye movements are tested in great detail, many normal adults and children will appear to have some minor difference. Those who specialise in this developmental testing believe that these subtle problems of eye function are in some way linked to learning difficulties.

Some of the ADD children in our care, who are weak readers, have been sent by their schools to developmental optometrists. Parents often return to our clinic angry that our hospital eye specialists failed to diagnose some significant defect. Many of these children are prescribed eye exercises or given low dioptre lenses. In our experience, few persist with these for more than a matter of months.

The American Academy of Pediatrics and the Australian College of Paediatrics have put out policy statements on vision and learning. In essence, they believe that for most children such treatments are of minimal or no benefit (see Appendix XVIII: Controversial therapies for ADD).

Tinted lenses

In the mid 1980s a Californian, Helen Irlen, patented certain lens tints which she claimed helped the reading disabled to read. The media responded enthusiastically with stories on '60 Minutes' on television and in major magazines. Few studies seem to have shown the success that was initially claimed. The very best results suggest that there is a small subgroup who might be helped, but in general the evidence seems unimpressive (see Appendix XVIII: Tinted lenses).

Multivitamins and zinc

In the early 1980s it was said that vitamin B6 benefited both inattentive and learning disabled children. Then zinc was claimed to help in ADD and autism. Now multivitamins have become popular.

There is no reputable research to show that any of these remedies has a significant effect on either ADD or its associated learning disabilities. Extra vitamins most certainly have a place in malnourishment and famine relief, but not in learning and behaviour.

Neurone entrapment—bio-feedback—sugar

We often see children who have attended alternative practitioners for cranial manipulation and realignment of the neck. The parents tell us that their child had impaired blood flow to the base of the brain or entrapment of a nerve inside the skull. Our specialist neurologists are 100 per cent certain there is no validity to these claims. If gentle pressure to the neck and skull can realign parts of the brain, our football heroes must lose a lot of learning on the pitch every week.

Bio-feedback is one of the newer techniques being promoted in North America. Occasionally, one sees it advertised in complementary health journals. The child watches a computer screen which shows a tracing of their brain wave activity. By modifying their way of working they then change the tracing, the theory being that you can retrain through feedback. Personally we have little experience of this but we know some of our American colleagues are very unhappy with this form of therapy.

Sugar is again under assault. One presumes it is part of our puritan upbringing, where anything which gives pleasure is probably evil. Parents often claim that replacing sugar with honey leads to better behaviour but this has been well researched and proven to be completely untrue. Honey is sugar, which has been recycled through a bee, with a number of nature's preservatives and pollutants added along the way. There is no doubt that sugar rots children's teeth and makes them fat, but there is no evidence it has any effect on learning or behaviour.

The Feingold Diet

In 1973, Dr Ben Feingold, a former Professor of Allergy in San Francisco, suggested a relationship between diet and hyper-activity. He went to the media with his startling but unproven theory, claiming that many artificial food additives, as well as some quite natural substances, were affecting the behaviour of our children. Specifically, he claimed that the reported rates of hyperactivity were increasing in proportion to the number of additives which legally pollute food. He told the press that his special diet could improve the behaviour in 50 per cent of these hyped-up little people. These claims had great repercussions as they were published in newspapers all around the world. The American government was obliged to set up committees to investigate the claims.

In the next decade, parents saw diet as the cornerstone of hyperactivity. Parent support groups were established all over Australia, most becoming so obsessed with food, that stimulant medication and other treatments were largely ignored.

Many parents still misunderstand what is meant by the Fein-gold Diet. It is not only about giving up chocolate, cola drinks, flavourings and colourings. It is also about avoiding nature's preservatives, for example, the natural salicylates which occur in foods, such as strawberries, tomatoes, oranges and pine-apples. Hidden preservatives can also be a problem as in sausages, salami and some 'extremely dead' dried meats. A few children even react to toothpaste, yeast extract and honey, or when they come in contact with it, perfume and dish-washing liquid.

The original Feingold Diet did have some inconsistencies. Pineapple juice was suggested as one of the safe drinks, when it is now known to be high in natural preservatives. (See also Appendix XIV.)

Exclusion diets

Today there are available much more reliable diets. These diets start by excluding all potentially harmful foods, placing the child and their family on a diet of water, pear juice, preservative free bread and unseasoned meats. Natural sugar syrup, such as Golden Syrup, has never been implicated in bad behaviour, so this is used in place of jams and spreads.

This strict diet is kept going for a number of weeks and if there is no significant improvement it is stopped. If the diet helps, the dietitian will gradually introduce other groups of food until those that are causing the harm have been clearly isolated. Finally, an individual diet is suggested which avoids the troublesome foods.

Note: all exclusion diets should be implemented and supervised by a dietitian or doctor specialising in this area. See Feingold's Original Diet (Appendix XIV) and the latest information on food chemicals and details of diet (Appendix XV).

Research into diet

Following Feingold's claims, an American Congressional Commission looked at the question of additives and encouraged research trials. Feingold had claimed that 50 per cent of children with behavioural problems would be helped by the diet. The question was whether this figure was correct and how much of this was a placebo effect. 'Placebo' is the term used for when, unknown to a patient, an inert substance is given instead of an active drug (for example, a sugar tablet instead of an aspirin). Studies show that one-third of people will believe that this non-treatment has made them feel somewhat better.

To combat the placebo effect, trials on diet had to be conducted 'completely blind'. That is, parents and others who observed the behaviours, could not know if the children were on or off the diet. Many methods were used including a sort of 'meals on wheels' where all food was delivered from outside the trial group's homes.

When 50 per cent who claimed to be helped by diet were challenged blindly with additives, only 1 in 10 showed any change in their behaviour. Most of the initial studies showed this 1 in 10 result. This represents 5 per cent of Feingold's initial claim of improvement in 50 per cent of the children.

Since that time there have been several studies which have reported a more impressive response (up to 60 per cent), but in most, the 5 per cent figure still stands. (See Appendix XVIII: Allergy, food additives and hyperactivity.)

Diet not specific for ADD

If diet affects behaviour, it does so in children whether they do, or do not, have ADD. It now seems that when diet works its main effect is on activity and irritability. There is little evidence that diet significantly alters the inattention, impulsivity and insatiability that are so troublesome in ADD.

The current view is that diet does affect some children, but a change in diet makes little difference to the trio of behaviours that cause most of the bother in ADD.

Our experience with diet

A number of parents in our practice certainly see changes with diet, but these are only with one or two clearly identified foods. Chocolate, cola, some cordials, and strawberries would be among the more common examples. It must be emphasised that this is a minority, and what's more the parents are usually quite clear as to the offending food so they avoid it. If there has been no obvious reaction to any one food, it is our experience that a strict exclusion diet will rarely bring any benefits.

(We must state that some colleagues, whom we greatly respect, strongly support diet and claim good results. They believe diet is particularly useful in the preschool child with ADD. They feel that those of us who have less success, do not follow the diet with sufficient dedication. We have no monopoly on opinion; parents must follow the path that shows them any significant success.)

Conclusion

It is tough for today's parents. Services to diagnose and treat ADD are seriously underfunded and overloaded. Finally, when treatment is provided, many children move ahead with painfully slow progress. While this happens frustrated parents grasp at any outside chance of help.

Parents should never be prevented from following any remedy they choose. All we ask is that the well-researched, proven treatments are used first, before resorting to those of debatable benefit.

Diet has a smaller part to play in the treatment of ADD than popular mythology might suggest. Diet never causes ADD, though in a minority of ADD and non-ADD children, certain foodstuffs may make their behaviour more active and possibly more irritable. There seems to be little evidence that diet directly affects attention, impulsivity or insatiability. Sugar has not been shown to cause bad behaviour. If parents wish to try a diet, they have our full support. All we ask is that they do it properly, under the supervision of a specialist doctor or dietitian.

11

Medication—the Facts

We make no apology for this book's support for stimulant medication. In the mid 1990s the use of these drugs in treating ADD is widely accepted. They are remarkably safe, and when prescribed properly, they are surprisingly free from side-effects. This form of therapy is so well proven, that it is no longer worth debating the point. (See Appendix XVIII for reviews of research.)

The medications

The stimulants Methylphenidate (Ritalin) and Dexamphetamine are the most commonly used and effective preparations for the treatment of ADD. When they fail to bring about a satisfactory response, the second line drugs are used—Imipramine (Tofranil), Clonidine (Catapres), Moclobemide (Aurorix) and Desipramine (Pertofran).

Of these alternative drugs, Clonidine is indicated when a child's activity and impulsivity is still causing problems despite the use of stimulant medication. As Clonidine appears to have little benefit in increasing attention it is often used in combination with Ritalin or Dexamphetamine. Tofranil, Aurorix and Pertofran improve attention, but their main effect is on the difficult behaviours of ADD. Tofranil and Pertofran are favoured when depression is also a problem (see Appendix XII).

For further information on Clonidine (Catapres), Imipramine (Tofranil), Desipramine (Pertofran) and Moclobemide (Aurorix) see Appendix XII.

The stimulants

The use of stimulant medications for treating ADD is not new. They were first shown to be effective in 1937. The benefits were recognised but stimulants were not widely used until the late 1950s, when the new preparation Methylphenidate (Ritalin) was first introduced.

In the last half century, parents have often been frightened away from considering stimulants through misinformation that branded them unsafe and their use controversial. The grounds for these antidrug opinions never came from any scientific source. They originated from a sensation-seeking media and the Citizens' Commission on Human Rights, a part of the

Church of Scientology. It is important for parents and professionals to distinguish between genuine controversy as opposed to beat-ups and authoritative ignorance (see Chapter 2).

At present, only three stimulant preparations are used: Methylphenidate (Ritalin), Dexamphetamine and Pemoline. It is said that these drugs are similar in effect, but most children will respond somewhat better to one medication than the other. For this reason when one preparation is ineffective or causes problems, the other should be tried. Ideally each drug should be trialled with every child, to ensure that the most effective medication is used.

The North Americans use a long-acting preparation of Ritalin (Ritalin Slow Release). This long-acting tablet is particularly useful for ADD adolescents whose esteem is eroded when they take their 'hyper' tablets each lunchtime. In the United Kingdom the datasheet on Methylphenidate (Ritalin) indicates that 'Ritalin is indicated as part of a comprehensive treatment programme for Attention Deficit Hyperactivity Disorder (ADHD) when remedial measures alone prove insufficient.'

The medication is available for prescribing as a controlled drug under Schedule 2 and the treatment needs to be under the supervision of a specialist in childhood behavioural disorders. It is supplied under a special procedure, which requires registration of the names of the patients with the pharmaceutical company.

Dexamphetamine sulphate is a controlled drug available on prescription under specialist supervision for the management of hyperactive children.

Pemoline is a central stimulant on normal prescription and Clonidine and the antidepressants are also available on normal prescription.

Stimulants—the effect

It seems a piece of faulty logic to give a stimulant medication to a child who is already overstimulated, but this is just what they need. The stimulants, or more correctly the psychostimulants, enhance the ADD child's natural abilities to select, focus, shut out distraction and think before they act. These medications are not sedatives, they do not dull a child's faculties, but they fine-tune what is already there to help them reflect and react in a much more normal way.

Stimulants—research findings

The benefits of stimulants have been studied extensively. Most researchers report significant improvement in 80 per cent of children with ADD. The worst figures we could find indicated a 60 per cent success rate, with the best a success rate of slightly over 90 per cent (see Appendix XVIII: The stimulants, p 220).

Studies have shown that stimulants reduce restlessness, help children to stick at a task, improve classroom productivity and increase accuracy in the children's work. Children are less impulsive, calmer and less disruptive, and interactions improve between the child, their parents, teachers and peers. There is also a significant improvement in the quality of the child's written work. Intelligence tests may be easier to administer when on medication, but there is no evidence that overall intellect is in any way altered.

Stimulants do not cure ADD

These drugs help our children to make the most of their abilities with regards to education, relationships and behaviour. The aim is to protect the family relationships, the child's esteem and their will to learn, until maturity brings some sort of natural resolution. For the majority of ADD children, there is a marked improvement which starts in the early teens (after age 12). When this change gets established some children will no longer require their medication.

Long-term benefits

There is no evidence that stimulants bring long-term benefits. It has been shown conclusively that stimulants provide a significant improvement in the short term, but long-term benefits are, as yet, presumed but not proven.

There is evidence that ADD children treated with medication are more likely to complete schooling and are less at risk of later substance abuse than their untreated friends, but that's as far as it goes.

Though long-term benefits have not yet been documented, it seems to us that positive results must eventually be shown. When medication works there is much less nagging, negativity and anger from parents. This mix of happier, less negative parents, with a more responsive and rewarding child, must provide a 'win-win' situation for all the players.

If these drugs can create a better academic, behavioural and social environment, today, this week, this month and this year, the chances are that these benefits will continue through future years. To be fair it must be noted that none of the alternative treatments (such as behavioural programs, diet, remedial education, psychiatric intervention, and so on) has proven long-term benefits either.

Side-effects — theoretical

The word amphetamine causes anxiety about addiction. Though used to treat the ADD child for over half a century, there is no evidence of addiction dependency or an increased risk of later substance abuse. Children, adolescents and even adults with ADD live their lives with an unfocused, muddled mind. When medication is effective, they can become more focused and aware. Humans take addictive drugs to escape from the real world, not to become more focused and aware.

Side-effects—easily reversible

Amphetamines can suppress *appetite* and cause weight loss. These side-effects are rarely a problem when the drug is taken with, or just after, a meal. Amphetamines may cause *wakefulness*, but this is a surprisingly rare side-effect in the correctly treated child. When stimulants cause a child to be slow to settle to sleep, this is easily remedied by reducing the last dose of medication given in the day. It must be remembered that some children with ADD find it hard to unwind enough to get to sleep, whether they are on or off medication. Some children in our care actually sleep better once we bring some order to their brain with medication.

Side-effects—genuine concerns

The main problem we encounter is children becoming *withdrawn, overfocused, teary* and *emotionally upset*. This only happens at the start of medication or when the dose is increased. If this does not occur when the dose is being introduced or raised, it will not happen later. It poses a particular problem when drugs are introduced in an inflexible, clumsy and poorly monitored way. These emotional side-effects are short-lived and should be resolved within four hours of suspending medication.

When a stimulant causes upset, the problem can be resolved by halving the dose or changing to the other preparation. When emotional well-being is not restored by a reduction in dose one author is quick to stop medication, while the other will persist if the problem is minor, realising that it usually reduces greatly within three weeks. *Rebound behaviour* can cause difficulties when the effects of medication start to wear off. If there is a behavioural blow-out as the peak drug level passes, this can be resolved by adding a small dose just before the time of the problem. Some children suffer from *headaches* on stimulants, and for a few this will prevent a particular preparation being used.

In the past growth retardation was said to be a side-effect of only those on high dose, long-term medication. In these children, if growth was reduced at all, it was thought to be at most 1 or 2 centimetres by adulthood. If this did happen it might be a small price to pay for the emotional gains in a child whose symptoms were so severe as to necessitate such a high dose. At present it is uncertain whether stimulants significantly affect growth and if they do, there seems to be a catch-up period when off the drugs, and there seem to be no growth concerns in the adolescent on stimulants. Growth seems to be either a minor problem or a non-problem, but we still keep accurate growth records, just to be sure.

The possibility of *tics* and *Tourette's syndrome* does cause concern. (Tics are involuntary twitches, usually of the eyes, face and neck. Tourette's syndrome involves major tics, odd involuntary mannerisms and, in some, inappropriate speech sounds.) It must be stated that ADD is strongly associated with tics and Tourette's syndrome, whether medication is given or not. Sometimes their appearance is unrelated to medication and on other occasions tics that were lying dormant seem to be activated by the prescription of stimulants. If tics seem to be increasing or there is any concern about the more major movements of Tourette's syndrome, suspend stimulants at once and contact your doctor. In the rare instances where major tics or Tourette's syndrome does appear following medication, this will usually resolve once medication is stopped. If there is a family history of these disorders, inform your doctor, as this may be a contra-indication to prescription.

See also Chapter 12 and Appendix XIII (The Stimulant Medications—Small Print Side-Effects).

Conclusion

The drugs Ritalin and Dexamphetamine have been extensively studied. About 80 per cent of school-age ADD children respond well to their use in the short term. These drugs are not sedatives which slow down a child's mind, instead they enhance the inattentive child's natural abilities and help them to focus, reflect and achieve better academically, socially and behaviourally.

Some people still state that there is controversy regarding the use of stimulants in treating ADD. In the mid-1990s most accept them as the single most effective form of therapy. Any professional who questions their use for this condition must be viewed as very out of touch with modern thinking. It is important not to confuse the word controversy with the word ignorance!

Summary: medication—the facts
The stimulants

Ritalin (Methylphenidate), 10 mg tablet.

Dexamphetamine, 5 mg tablet.

Pemoline, 20 mg tablet or as syrup.

Others

Catapres (Clonidine): Helps activity and impulsivity but not inattention.

Tofranil (Imipramine): Helps most ADD behaviours and has some effect on inattention.

Pertofran (Desipramine): Helps most ADD behaviours and has some effect on inattention.

Aurorix (Moclobemide): Helps most ADD behaviours and has some effect on inattention.

- Stimulants enhance normal brain function.

- Helps focus attention and allows children to think before they act.

- Effective in about 80 per cent of children with ADD (studies show between 60 per cent and 90 per cent).

- Stimulants do not cure ADD.

- Helps focus attention and allows children to think before they act.

- Effective in about 80 per cent of children with ADD (studies show between 60 per cent and 90 per cent).

- Stimulants do not cure ADD.

- Addiction is not a problem in ADD.

- Appetite reduction and sleep problems can occur, but are easily corrected.

- Emotional upset, tears and withdrawn behaviour can happen if the dose is too high or the wrong preparation used.

- Behaviour sometimes rebounds as the drug starts to wear off.

- These drugs are short-acting: they start working in a quarter to half an hour and wear off in three to five hours.

- One Ritalin tablet (10 mg) is almost equal to one Dex-amphetamine tablet (5 mg).

- Many children will respond better to one preparation than the other. Both are usually trialled.

- If side effects are troublesome on one drug, try the other.

- Stimulants are the single most effective form of therapy in ADD.

- Behaviour modification and educational interventions are important, but usually work better in conjunction with stimulants.

- A lot of misinformation has appeared in the media concerning these medications.

- It is parents—not doctors, psychologists or educationalists—who decide if medication will be started, continued or suspended.

- Medication will continue for as long as parents see significant benefits. This may be six months, six years or even into adulthood.

12

Medication — Practical Prescribing

Before considering stimulants for the treatment of ADD children, let's be quite clear who is in charge. Parents, not doctors, decide if they want a trial of medication and when it should be continued or stopped. The drugs will be given while a parent sees major benefits and no side-effects. When there is doubt as to their effectiveness, or the slightest concern over side-effects, parents will stop the drug and shout for help. We make this point as anti-drug activists frequently claim that children are unnecessarily put on stimulants while parents see absolutely no benefits, only side-effects. This is ridiculous: if it were any other drug, a parent would call for help or stop its use.

To prescribe or not to prescribe

The official teaching on stimulant medication, states that they should not be used until behavioural, educational and family programs have been put in place. From our experience, these other therapies are of some benefit by themselves, but when given in conjunction with stimulants, they become many times more effective. For this reason we usually start stimulants and our behaviour programs at the same time.

There is no clear-cut point at which one knows that stimulants should be prescribed. It all depends on the severity of the ADD, the predominant behaviours and how well both parents and school are coping. Where education, home relationships and self-esteem are suffering, we would strongly suggest a medication trial.

A clinical trial

There is only one reliable test which will predict the likelihood of success of stimulants and that is to give a carefully controlled clinical trial. If it works, you prescribe and if it doesn't, you don't.

Some practitioners use the Paired Associate Learning or Continuous Performance Tests to measure memory and persistence before any medication is given and later to measure its effect. This quantifies the size of improvement and provides guidance as to the best drug to prescribe (see also Appendix VI).

In our practice we work in a much simpler way: we listen to parents. The medication is always started over a weekend, so that the parents are around to observe any benefits or possible side-effects. One drug is started on the first weekend and the second drug is trialled on the next weekend. If the benefits are not clear the drugs are then alternated: three days of one drug, three days off medication, three days of the other drug, and so on, until both the parents and school give us a clear statement as to the success or failure of both drugs.

During a trial the drug is usually given twice a day but it can be given once. All we need to know is whether the drug works in the four hours while it is active after the dose is given, and if there are side-effects. When we know it is successful, we can adjust the dosage to suit the individual needs of that child.

Stimulants — short-acting drugs

The benefits of Ritalin and Dexamphetamine are almost immediate and last for a very short time. After taking a tablet the behaviour will start to change in 15 to 30 minutes and the benefits will be lost between three and five hours. This means that most ADD school children take a dose of medication with breakfast, another at the start of the lunch break and a smaller dose at 3.30 pm to help with afternoon behaviour and homework.

It is extremely important for those monitoring the benefits of these drugs to be aware of this short span of action. If a tablet is given at breakfast and behaviour deteriorates dramatically in the afternoon, then the child is not on active medication at this time of trouble. This is not a failure of medication, it is an indication of the need for a second or third dose for this child.

Approximately two-thirds of our school-age ADD children are maintained on three tablets a day. Most of the others take two, and a few require four doses a day, as they seem to metabolise the drug very quickly. Dexamphetamine is said to be a slightly longer-acting drug than Ritalin, but in our experience there doesn't seem to be much difference between them.

The measurable benefits disappear after about four hours, but a little stimulant remains in the blood for up to twelve hours. In this low dose it gives no behavioural benefit but when the second and third dose of the day are given on the tail of the previous tablet, it may allow these later doses to be slightly smaller.

With or without food

Until recently it was believed that stimulants should be given a quarter of an hour before food. Now we are told it is just as effective and far more convenient to give the drug with meals.

Stimulants may suppress appetite and where possible are best avoided in the two hours before a major meal.

Starting stimulants

Ritalin comes as a 10 mg tablet, while Dexamphetamine is available as a 5 mg tablet. Essentially these are equal, tablet for tablet. The dose required is a very individual matter and though not directly proportional to body weight, guidelines always use this as a measure. Ritalin is given up to a maximum dose of 1.5 mg per kilogram body weight per day. The maximum dose of Dexamphetamine is half this amount, at 0.75 mg per kilogram body weight per day. Most of our patients are well maintained using 50 per cent to 60 per cent of these maximum levels.

Most practitioners prescribe using half or whole tablets, but we encourage the use of quarter tablet increments, particularly in the younger child. Often we find a child is undertreated on half a tablet, may have side-effects on one tablet and is just right on three-quarters of a tablet.

It must be remembered that stimulants are remarkably free of side-effects and almost all the troubles come at the start of treatment or when doses are increased. If you get it right at the beginning, it should stay right. What's more, children are not supposed to build up a tolerance to these drugs; if the dose is correct at the start, the same dose will do for years. Although this is the teaching on stimulants, and it is essentially true, occasionally one of our children seems to stop responding for no apparent reason. When tolerance appears, we suspend the medication and observe what happens. Often the benefits may have reduced, but they are still seen to be significant.

Stimulants—what parents notice

When medication is effective, parents tell us that their child may be:

- Better able to stick at a task.
- Less impulsive (they think before they act or speak).
- Less insatiable (they don't go on and on, nag less and can let a matter drop).
- Less restless, fidgety and 'full on'.
- More reachable.
- Changed, so that home life becomes calmer.

Stimulants—what teachers tell us

When stimulants are effective the school may notice that the ADD child is:

- Less distractible, disruptive and fidgety.
- Able to get work finished without the need to be stood over.
- Producing neater written work which is more consistent, better organised and has fewer mistakes.
- Showing improvement in playground behaviour.
- Relating better to other children and is socially more in tune.

When school is offside

Many schools and senior educationalists have been vigorously opposed to the use of medication. But times are changing, and there is now a new awareness of ADD with some schools starting to accept the benefits of stimulant medication. There are, however, still a few antistimulant stalwarts and it is an unfortunate state of affairs when parents are obliged to introduce medication without the knowledge of the school. When there are difficulties, first we introduce the stimulants at home and if the response is good the ADD child can then start to take them at school.

If the teacher is approachable they are informed that a trial will take place over the next few weeks and are asked to record every morning the behaviour and work achieved. One dose of medication is given at breakfast for three days, then stopped for two days and this on–off regime is continued as a blind trial, where the teacher does not know which mornings the drug is being given and which it is not.

When the school are completely offside, the same system is followed without informing any school staff. If medication is successful, you soon see a pattern of good and bad days, and merit awards. Armed with this evidence an appointment is made to discuss the matter.

When antimedication attitudes are impossibly entrenched, the drug is given before leaving home and the lunchtime dose is slipped into a hollow jelly bean or marshmallow. The parents are amused when the merit awards start to appear, but this is their secret. We must emphasise that these secretive suggestions are rarely required in these enlightened times. *In fact we make a plea to all parents reading this book to keep their child's school informed and fully aware of all that is happening.*

How long to treat?

Stimulants are required for as long as the parents continue to see significant benefits. For a few this will be six months, others two years, and for many the benefits will last until the end of school. As the use of these medications in adulthood becomes more accepted it is likely that some of today's children will take stimulants for part of their adult lives.

The parents in our care are asked to continually monitor the benefits of stimulants. Every parent forgets to give medication from time to time and these lapses provide on-going feedback as to the need for stimulants. If there is little change when a dose is missed, it is time to stop. When there is any doubt we suggest that the drug be suspended for one week, reintroduced for a week and suspended again. By this method both parents and teachers quickly know if it is necessary to continue. When stimulants are stopped this can be done immediately without any gradual tail-off.

Remember the first words of this chapter. *You, the parents, are in charge. You, with the advice of the school, tell us whether medication will or will not be continued. It is your decision.*

Do you need holidays off medicine?

Some suggest weekends and holidays should be lived without medication. If behaviour is a significant problem we never stop stimulants at home. There is no evidence that properly monitored, long-term medication will harm children. However, it is certain that untreated ADD children can do immense, long-term damage to their family relationships and to their own happiness. These long-term, emotional repercussions are very real and though ideally there should be frequent holidays off medication, for most ADD children this will not be the case.

Are stimulants completely safe?

There is no such thing as a completely safe drug but as medicines go these are well researched and free of major problems. Appendix XIII gives a list of all the possible but rare side-effects.

As with any form of treatment the benefits need to be balanced against any possible problems. Remember that every day people die from the effects of over the counter drugs like aspirin. People can even have heart palpitations after drinking tea or coffee. Nothing in this world is 100 per cent safe, but please don't let the antistimulant activists so frighten you with fine print that you miss the main message.

Prescribing stimulants—sample regimes

There are many possible ways to prescribe these medications. For your interest, here are some examples of the sorts of regimes that we use in our practice. Parents should follow the regime their practitioner prescribes.

A four-year-old child

- Start with a quarter of a tablet in the morning and, if there are no side effects, one-quarter of a tablet at midday
- Maintain on:
    Half a tablet twice daily, or
    Half a tablet three times daily, or
    Three-quarters of a tablet in the morning, half a tablet at midday and one-quarter of a tablet at 3.30 pm

A six-year-old child

- Start with half a tablet in the morning and, if there are no side-effects, half a tablet at midday
- Maintain on:
    Three-quarters of a tablet or one tablet in the morning.

Half a tablet, three-quarters of a tablet or one tablet at midday
Half a tablet may or may not need to be given at 3.30 pm

A 12-year-old child

- Start with half a tablet in the morning and, if there are no side-effects, half a tablet at midday. Next day the dose can be doubled.

- Maintain on:
  One, one-and-a-half or two tablets in the morning
  One, one-and-a-half or two tablets at midday
  One tablet at 3.30 pm

Stimulant therapy—trouble shooting

The prescribing doctor will advise how to fine-tune the medication to avoid any problems. Here are a few suggestions we give to the parents in our practice.

- *Behaviour rebounds as levels drop*
  Add an additional small dose, for example, at 11.00 am or 3.30 pm.

- *The young child of three to six years who metabolises the drug too quickly*
  Give four small doses each day, for example, 8.00 am, 11.00 am, 3.30 p.m. The first dose of the day should be slightly larger than the rest.

- *Behaviour problems in the playground*
  Take the midday tablet at the beginning of, or half an hour before, the lunch break.

- *Impossible early morning behaviour*
  Give medication on waking. An additional small mid-

morning dose may be required to maintain acceptable behaviour until lunchtime.

- *Drugs cause difficulty getting to sleep*
  Suspend or reduce the 3.30 pm dose.
  If this is still a problem, reduce the midday dose.

- *Appetite reduction and weight loss*
  Give drug with meals.
  Reduce or stop afternoon dose to allow for a large evening meal.
  If weight and appetite are still a concern the total dose can be reduced or a different drug used.

- *Homework hassles*
  Give a 3.30 pm dose.

- *Emotionally unstable, overfocused, teary*
  Halve the dose. Suspend medication or change medication.
  When symptoms are mild, some medical practitioners suggest that you persevere for three weeks, which often allows time for most problems to pass.

- *An ADD child has epilepsy or intellectual retardation*
  Stimulants can be given with care to the ADD child with epilepsy.
  Stimulants are occasionally indicated for use with the retarded child if the behaviour is grossly outside the normal for the child's developmental age.

- *Inattention causes problems in academic learning, not behaviour*
  Medication is given only for school and homework.

- *Behaviour problems, both at school and home*
  Give medication every school day, weekend and holiday for as long as the benefits continue.

- *School or parents feel the benefits have gone*
  Stop medication for one week, then reintroduce for one

week, then stop again. Observe what happens and make a decision.

● *Listen to the child*
Doctors must be sure that the child, as well as the parents, is happy with the effects (and side-effects) of medication.

13

The Associated Problems of Learning and Language

Children with ADD frequently have associated weaknesses in reading, spelling, writing, mathematics and language. The incidence of these specific learning problems is usually quoted at about 50 per cent, meaning that 50 per cent of ADD children also have these related problems, though some say it is as low as 10 per cent and others as high as 90 per cent (see Appendix XVIII: Comorbidity, Semrud–Clikeman, M.).

ADD by itself causes children to underfunction academically for their intellect through inattention, poor memory and lack of impulse control. When these problems are combined with specific learning disabilities, the child is faced with double trouble.

Attention, memory and executive control

Inattention (lack of attention) is probably the most common reason for a child not achieving their full potential at school. Attention is quite a complicated concept. One of the many possible ways to understand it is to divide it into a number of overlapping parts such as *selectivity, monitoring, maintaining effort* and *executive control*. These parts are in turn closely associated with memory.

Attention
Inappropriate selectivity

Children with ADD find it hard to see the wood for the trees. When information comes in they pick up on one small part of it but don't identify the main message. In answering a question they go off on a tangent and get side-tracked. When attempting projects or exam questions they spend all their time colouring in their diagram and don't get on with the answer. If we can't wisely select what to give our attention to, we can't succeed at school.

Inadequate self-monitoring

Children need to attend well if they are to spot the errors before the teacher who is marking their school work. When they write, ADD children make silly mistakes which are not noted in their inattentive rush. When reading aloud to the class, they blurt out a word without checking if it matches the meaning of the sentence. Inattention is partly to blame for this but there are also the problems of poor self-monitoring and impulsivity. This lack of quality control leaves many ADD children underfunctioning for their true academic ability.

Inability to maintain effort

The inattentive pupil finds it impossible to stick at an uninteresting task. They become bored and don't pay attention to schoolwork, while a fast-moving video game will hold their attention for hours. This lack of persistence and switching off from difficult schoolwork is a particular problem in the primary school years.

Mental fatigue is a big problem in the ADD child. Complicated work requires so much concentration they soon suffer 'terminal brain fade'. These children can maintain such effort, but it is at great personal cost. It is no wonder they don't want to start their homework or to see the tutor waiting for them when they arrive home after school.

Memory

It is hard to distinguish between problems of attention and memory. If we can't attend to the work in front of us, it cannot be photographed by our minds, integrated and stored away. Children with ADD usually have a good long-term memory but a poor recall for the present. They remember what happened a year ago, but not the information that has just been given.

Short-term memory

Most ADD children are no good at remembering instructions.

They forget large chunks of what is being taught and have particular problems when information is given in a sequence. This shows up as a poor memory for lists and confusion with the steps required to solve a problem.

Active working memory

This part of short-term memory refers to a child's ability to hold a number of bits of information in the mind, so they may be processed. If you can't keep several groups of figures in your head at one time, mental arithmetic is impossible. If we are to understand what we read, the words at the beginning of the paragraph must still be remembered by the time we reach the end of the paragraph. With language, active working memory helps us to juggle words in our minds so that we can craft them to make the maximum impact upon use in our speech and written language.

Executive control

Animals do not usually think before they respond, but humans do usually reflect before they react. This difference is due to executive control, which is a function of areas around the frontal lobes of the human brain. These areas are the conductor that keeps the orchestra of learning and behaviour playing in harmony. Children with ADD have a weakness in this area that results in problems of prioritising, planning, using time wisely, anticipating consequences, learning from the past and staying in tune socially. This not only affects behaviour, it also causes the ADD child to underfunction at school.

Specific learning difficulties

Children with ADD are already disadvantaged by their problems of attention, memory, and executive control. To make life even more difficult, many also have a specific learning disability. The most common of these is a weakness in the areas of reading, spelling, writing, mathematics and language. Children who have ADD without the impulsive overactive package of behaviours (ADD without H) have a higher incidence of these learning difficulties than those with the more recognisable presentation of ADD with H.

Reading and spelling
How we learn to read

The first step in reading is to learn some 'sight words'. This recognition starts at preschool age as children see street signs, advertisements and everyday labels. Soon they recognise their own name and words such as stop, walk, McDonald's, Coca-Cola, Toyota.

Children entering school vary greatly in the number of words they can recognise and this skill increases rapidly throughout the kindergarten year. The ability to recognise words by their shape is an important part of adult speed reading, but before we get to this level we must move through some very complicated steps.

To be a proficient reader the next skill required is the ability to decode new, unfamiliar words by breaking them down into their component parts. The first step is to learn each letter of the alphabet. The next step is to associate the correct sound with each of these letters (sound symbol association). The letter 'b' in the alphabet is called 'bee', but sounds out as 'buh'. The first stage in reading phonetically is to associate a sound with every letter of the alphabet.

Next a child learns to look at a word and break it up into its individual sounds (segmentation). Speech pathologists tell us that the smallest unit of sound is called a phoneme, therefore this ability to segment a word and be aware of the phonemes is called phonemic segmentation and phonemic awareness. As a child looks at the word 'cat' they must now learn that it is made up of three sounds — 'ku', 'aa', 'tuh'. They then start to blend two sounds together, for example: 'ca', 'at' ('ku-aa', 'aa-tuh') and also two consonants (consonant blends), such as 'pl' and 'tr'.

Once they have mastered breaking down words the child moves on to learn those that don't fit the simple sound rules. Diphthongs are where two vowels come together to make one sound, for example, 'oi' in 'oil' and 'ou' in 'out'. Consonant diagraphs are where two letters join to make a different sound, for example, 'th', 'sh', 'ch', 'ph', 'gh'.

Finally, children have to learn anomalies, where groups of letters sound different from word to word, for example, '**gh**ost', 'tou**gh**', 'cat', 'call'.

The child uses these newfound rules to sort out the sounds they see, then blends them to make a meaningful word: 'c-a-t' means 'cat'. After this it is just a matter of time, practice and inherent ability that turns one into a strong reader.

Good adult readers skim through the text using an advanced form of shape recognition helped by cues from the context, the grammar and pictures. Adults who are fast, natural readers can't understand why dyslexic children switch off the moment they see the print. When you realise how complicated the process is, it is no wonder!

Reading difficulties

The majority of children with reading problems have difficulties with phonemic awareness and segmentation, the ability to recognise and break words into the component sounds. A smaller number of weak readers have trouble with shape recognition, which is the skill needed for effective sight reading. A third group are doubly disadvantaged with problems in both the above areas (the mixed type).

Children whose weakness is phonemic awareness will do well in the early stages of learning to read when shape recognition is all that is needed. They quickly come unstuck when they have to sound out what they see. Children with this sort of reading problem look at the word 'cat' and see only one sound rather than three. Eventually they proceed beyond this simple sounding out, but then it starts to get really complicated with all the rules and variations that can make reading difficult. When children have this problem with sounding out, they are taught reading by building on their shape recognition skills and teaching them to use grammar, context and pictures to tune them into the meaning.

Weak readers who can sound out words may have difficulty at shape recognition, and are said to have visual perceptual dyslexia. They are slow to develop a sight word vocabulary and, as they have to sound out each word, their reading is slow. They start out with problems in the basic building blocks, confusing 'b's with 'd's. Clever teachers develop these skills with prompts, for example, the letter 'b' is made up of a bat before a ball. The letter 'd' has a drum before a stick.

When children have a mixed type of reading difficulty, teachers have to use anything that works.

If it is not already enough to have a specific weakness in reading, in addition there are the problems of ADD. Even if the words are correctly decoded, poor active working memory lets the meaning get lost by the end of the sentence. With poor self-monitoring the appropriateness of a word in a sentence is not checked. Finally, they spend so much time decoding, unravelling, looking at individual words and trying to understand the meaning, that the effort is not maintained and they lose interest. With so much mental energy required for so little success, it is no wonder weak readers will make any excuse to avoid heavy literature (see also Chapters 14 and 15, Hints to Help With Weak Reading and Language and Appendix XVI, Practical Ways to Help Handwriting.

Mathematics

Problems with mental arithmetic are almost universal in ADD children and on top of this quite a number have a specific learning weakness in the area of the mechanics of mathematics (dyscalculia). With this problem the child has difficulty sorting out relative size, understanding the processes needed to add, subtract, multiply and divide, as well as the concepts needed for algebra and other subjects. Dyscalculia is like dyslexia. It is part of the child's make-up and no amount of tutoring will turn the weak student into an advanced mathematician. For some reason specific learning difficulties in maths are frequently associated with problems of handwriting.

Learning mathematics

The first step in becoming a mathematician takes place around the age of two and a half years, when little children start to repeat numbers in a meaningless, parrot-like fashion, called rote counting. By the time they arrive in preschool, the child has learnt to attach meaning to the numbers. With this skill they can look at a picture and count the three fish or look at their fingers and count to ten. This is called correspondence counting. Now they know the relative sizes of numbers, realising that four is more than three.

Once school starts children learn the basics of addition and subtraction (maths operations). Then figures are written in columns, to be added and subtracted. The times tables are memorised, followed by learning multiplication and division. Now they move to fractions, decimals, algebra, geometry and then on to all the more complicated concepts (abstract numerical reasoning).

Children with ADD usually have little difficulty in repeating numbers parrot-fashion by rote and can correspondence count using their fingers to count to ten, but when fingers and objects can no longer be used as a calculator, they are in trouble.

To manage maths we need to be organised and to have a good active working memory. Without this we lose track of what we are adding, borrowing, subtracting and multiplying, and mental arithmetic is a non-event.

Many ADD children have dyscalculia. They are slow to grasp the relative size of figures, to learn tables, to remember the correct sequence of digits, to understand the meaning of mathematical signs, to master fractions and to comprehend the concepts of higher mathematics. It is sometimes unclear whether there is a pure specific disability in the area of mathematics or whether the problem is mostly inattention and memory. Whatever the cause, the result is the same. Most ADD children find mathematics is far from fun.

Language problems

In the 1990s there is great interest in the way language is associated with ADD and reading. Children with ADD often have a particular pattern of speech and many of the problems of reading come from a difficulty in the decoding of language in the brain.

Learning language

In the months before their first birthday a baby's tuneful babble turns to speech-like sounds. Between the ages of one and two they attach meaning to each sound and have a large, single word vocabulary.

Around the second birthday they learn the relationships between words, and how to put them together in phrases and then sentences. Over the next year they start to add grammar and then to plan and organise their ideas into a simple narrative.

As they leave the toddler years children learn the rules of two-way conversation. They listen, wait and respond in a socially appropriate way. By school they start to tune in to unspoken cues and know what is and is not acceptable. By the end of primary school, language has become much more complex, such as talking around the subject using innuendo, riddles and jokes.

The understanding part of speech starts just before the first birthday when they find the word 'no' means 'no'. By 14 months they may respond to simple commands such as 'point to your nose' or 'close the door'. After age two, ideas such as 'bigger', 'smaller', 'up', 'down' are taken aboard and they start to cope with more than one item of information at a time. From here the child moves on to more abstract concepts, for example, 'If you had a dog, a hen and a fish, which one would have hair?' Finally, they start to understand all the subtleties which are hidden in double meanings, our intonation and in what we don't quite say.

There is a great difference between the simple question/ answer language of the young child, for example, 'Show me the fire station', and the language that is used by those who express and comprehend really well, for example, 'Why can't you park the car in front of the fire station door?' Children may be familiar with quite a lot of words and have learned many answers but they may still be quite disabled by their lack of high level language.

The difficulties with attention, active working memory and executive control cause most of the concerns with language.

ADD children don't listen before they respond. They impatiently break into others' conversations. They are disorganised, so their speech frequently slips off-track and they skip from one topic to another. With their problems of selectivity they get caught up in unimportant detail, become side-tracked and miss the big picture. Stories are punctuated by long pauses, 'umms' and 'ahhs' which often hide a problem of finding the right word. When you ask questions they answer, 'Good', 'I don't know', 'I can't remember', rather than struggling to organise their substandard speech. When it comes to comprehension ADD children have problems with sequencing, for example, 'before', 'after', 'yesterday', 'tomorrow'.

With these language problems, many ADD children are unable to maintain a proper two-way conversation. They can't regulate the content to the needs of the listener, so people switch off. This difficulty with the social use of language is referred to as a problem of pragmatic skills (see also Chapters 14 and 15, Hints to Help With Reading and Language Problems).

Conclusion

About half of all children with ADD also have some specific learning weakness in an area such as reading, writing, spelling or language. On top of this almost all have problems with attention, selectivity, memory, monitoring and impulse control. These problems of specific learning weakness become so intertwined with difficulties of ADD that we find them hard to see separately. The exact proportion of the blend may be uncertain, but there is no dispute about the end result. Children with ADD usually underfunction academically for their intellect.

Summary: the learning problems of ADD
Poor attention span

- Inappropriate selection (off tangent, can't see wood for trees).

- Inadequate self monitoring (poor checking and quality control).

- Inability to maintain effort (loses interest, quickly bored, mentally fatigued).

Poor memory

- Short-term memory (instructions forgotten, half heard messages).

- Active working memory (trouble holding several pieces of information in mind, mental arithmetic, speech and reading problems).

Lack of executive control

- Poor planning and use of time (difficulty anticipating, prioritising and staying in tune socially).

The specific learning problems
Reading delay

- Problems of phonetics (difficulty sounding out words).
- Problems of sight word reading (difficulty recognising words by their shape).
- A mixed reading problem (both phonetics and sight word reading).
- Problem of comprehension (understanding what is read).
- ADD reading problems (impulsive, poor self monitoring and active working memory).

Mathematics weak

- Dyscalculia (poor concept of size, slow to learn tables and master concepts of maths).
- ADD problems with maths (lose track, disorganised, poor self monitoring, sequence difficulty. Poor active working memory effects mental arithmetic).

Language problems and ADD

- Expressive speech (slips off track, loses sequence, use of blocking words, for example, 'Don't know').
- Social language (interrupts, mis-answers, poor eye contact, miss social cues).
- Comprehension (information lost with inattention, poor selectivity and active working memory).

14

Hints to Help with Reading

Many ADD children also have a developmental reading disorder (dyslexia), which in our experience is usually of hereditary origin. This inheritance follows an interesting pattern in families. If a person has either pure ADD or pure dyslexia, it usually passes to the next generation in this same form. If ADD is associated with dyslexia, those that inherit the dyslexia will generally also have double trouble.

Reading problems

The way we learn to read was discussed in detail in Chapter 13. There we noted how dyslexia could present in four possible ways:

- A weakness with phonetics (sounding out words).
- A weakness with sight words (recognising words by shape).
- A mixed reading problem (phonetics and sight words).
- A weakness with reading comprehension (understanding what is read).

With these problem areas in mind parents should promote reading by first strengthening the child's strong points and from this firm foundation then working on the weak points. Here are some of our suggestions.

Ways to encourage sound recognition

- First teach the child the letters of the alphabet.
- Next link each letter with its sound (sound symbol association), for example, the letter 'u' sounds 'uh'.
- Strengthen this sound symbol skill by associating this letter with pictures that start with the sound, for example, the letter 'u' sounds out as 'uh', as in 'umbrella'.
- The next stage is to memorise the sounds of certain word clusters. These word clusters are the diphthongs ('ae', 'ou', 'ei', 'oo', 'ee') and the consonant diagraphs ('ch', 'ph', 'gh', 'th'). These cannot be deciphered by sounding out and can only be mastered by constant practice.
- Now you must go back to the basic sounds, and teach the child how to blend two together, for eample, 'tu', 'wi', 'ca',

'wu' and 'ft', 'lt', 'gr', 'pl'. These give the basic building blocks for creating words.

- Combinations of letters can now be blended, for example, 'tu' → 'tuf' → 'tuft'; 'wi' → 'wil' → 'wilt'.

- Blending can be helped by using a box framework, which puts each letter of a word in a box, like one sees in a crossword puzzle. This focuses attention on one letter at a time and keeps the sequence in order.

- Teach the child to see each word as a number of component sounds which come in a set order. To help this they can count out the syllables or tap out the parts they can hear in a word, for example, the word 'envelope' (en-vel-ope) has three parts.

- Teach the child to divide big words into little words, for example, skate-board, post-box, fish-tank, out-side, sun-light, butter-fly.

- The focus continues on the individual sounds in words. Ask them to isolate the sounds at the beginning, end, and any named position within a word, for example, what is the beginning sound in the word 'leg'? 'L'-eg. What sound is in the fourth position of 'strip'? str-'I'-p. Children can again be helped by presenting words in a box framework. This enables them to focus on each sound, one at a time.

- As parents we can read, talk and work with our children to help sort out the sounds of words, but often it takes more than this. Remedial reading tutors can be recommended through a school or a parent support group.

- Some parents engage a speech pathologist to help improve their child's ability to discriminate sounds. One of many programs used for assessment is the Lindamood Auditory Conceptualisation Test. This uses coloured blocks to represent units of sound and through its companion method, the Auditory Discrimination In-depth Remedial Program, the child is trained to segment words in readiness for reading. This strengthens one step in the reading process.

- The enthusiasm of parents and teacher is important in keeping the child interested in the written word during the remedial process.

Ways to encourage word recognition

- Make up some index cards, each representing one important word (flashcards). Ask the child to view them regularly and introduce more words when the first ones are learnt.
- Expand their sight vocabulary by teaching lists of phonetic and non-phonetic words in their word families, for example:

bat	hat	cat	fat	sat	pat	rat	mat
sight	light		might		tight		bight

- Play word recognition games with flashcards along the lines of the card game Snap.
- Certain spelling rules need to be learnt, for example the silent 'k' ('**k**nock', '**k**nee') and the silent 'e' ('chees**e**', 'goos**e**').
- Spelling can be helped using games such as Junior Scrabble.
- When you are reading a story to the child, cover the print in mid-story and ask them to use the grammar, context and pictures to guess the next word.
- The above steps are helpful, but most sight word recognition comes as we read simple stories with our children.

Ways to encourage sound and word recognition

When both phonetic and sight word parts of reading are weak (mixed reading problem) we have to take from all the above techniques to help the child's reading. There is usually one part of reading which is stronger so start by building on this, then they can fall back on it. With these children the secret is to go with whatever seems to work. Stress the positives, don't dwell on the negatives.

Ways to help reading comprehension

Children who find reading difficult can spend so much mental energy decoding the words that they miss the meaning. This defeats the purpose as there is no point reading the sentence if we don't understand what it means. Comprehension can be improved by doing the following:

- Select high interest books written at the right level for the child.
- Presenting reading material in manageable sized chunks. Don't give them more than they are able to digest.
- With the correctly sized portions, encourage the child to actively think about what they have read and then talk about it before they move on.
- In the early stages of reading it is often best for the parent to read and ask questions about comprehension as you go along. Stop every now and then so that the child may read a word. As time goes on, give them longer chunks to read.
- When the child gets stuck with a word they can't understand ask them to identify it, based on the grammar and context. Also point out any illustrations to see if they act as a word prompt.
- Interest is very important, so choose books carefully. The child will be more motivated if the topic is of interest to them. Start with few words and lots of pictures.
- Don't be afraid to read the same storybook several times. It all helps.
- Don't be in a hurry as you read with your child. Children

with reading difficulty need time to work out the words and understand the message.

- As reading becomes stronger children should be encouraged to give you a summary of what they have read.

- Try to have a regular reading time every day, preferably just before bedtime when the house is quiet.

- Keep the reading material well within the child's abilities. While they are succeeding they feel encouraged and are spurred onto greater things.

- There are now some good computer programs which can be used to develop reading, spelling, writing and mathematic skills. Some parents swear by these, but we must not forget that even the most expensive program will give more pain than pleasure to children with these learning difficulties.

- As well as parents helping comprehension, teachers and re-medial tutors can work wonders. There are also some speech pathologists who promote, amongst other techniques, the Lindamood Visualising and Verbalising Program. This trains the child to build up a mental picture of what they are read-ing, then talk about the image in their mind.

- As in all parts of learning, parents are important teachers. Teaching the weak reader can be slow and extremely frus-trating, but go gently. Pushing can become a great turn-off for the struggling reader.

  Increase the motivation to read by choosing a topic which is of interest to the child. Don't worry if the same book is read many times and the one topic 'done to death'.

  Select high interest books which are written at the right level for this child.

  Interact as you read, stopping every now and then so they may read a word. As time goes on longer chunks will be given to read.

As you read, encourage them to tune in to the pictures, the context and the grammar so they have something to fall back on should their phonetic and sight word skills let them down. When reading is difficult every little prompt helps.

A common problem

A weakness in reading is extremely common in the child with ADD. It is not that they are lazy, stupid or poorly taught, they just find the effort of reading gives little pleasure. Where the difficulty is in decoding the sounds, the word recognition skills must be boosted while the sounds are slowly sorted out. Where word recognition is a problem the phonetic skills of reading should be boosted while flashcards and constant practice improve the recognition skills.

Even when reading appears to be quite good there is often so much effort put into the reading that much of the meaning is missed.

Please be patient. Children with major reading problems frequently continue to have some reading weakness no matter what technique is used. Read, talk, question and never push too hard. A patient parent is the top teacher.

15

Language Problems

Language problems are more common with ADD than most people realise and there seems very little published information on practical ways to help. When it came to writing this chapter, we sat down with our speech pathologist colleagues and pinpointed the main difficulties we saw in our ADD children. In simple terms there seem to be six problem areas we are trying to help:

- Speech slips off on a tangent.
- Problems with sequence.
- Communication which is socially out of tune.
- Difficulty comprehending long instructions.
- Picking up on the wrong part of the message.
- Difficulty with vague, open-ended questions.

This may look a very learned list, but don't be fooled: it is much easier to describe the problems we see, than to make them disappear. Here are our top tips to help.

Ways to keep speech on track

Children with ADD are impulsive, inattentive and disorganised. When talking they may ramble on, become sidetracked away from the topic, or get stuck on some unimportant detail.

- When the topic of their speech is drifting off on a tangent, gently steer them back to the main topic.
- Use verbal prompts to give the speech structure: 'You were telling me about whales. What was it they ate?'
- Rehearse their speech by playing games: 'Now you are on the latest TV games show. We each get a topic and you must talk about it for 20 seconds.'
- Take time to listen and appear interested.
- Encourage clear communication, but never become a nit-picking parent.

Ways to strengthen the presentation of information in sequence

Presenting information in sequence is a particular problem. As the ADD child tells us some exciting event, the end may be at the beginning, the middle at the end, and the start is nowhere. It is hard to be an interested listener when language is so jumbled and out of order.

- First, work out what was meant to have been said and then gently encourage the child to go back and have another go.
- Organise the child by asking specific questions: 'So what were you doing when it started?' 'Who was first to see it?' 'What happened next?'
- Sequence is something we teach our children in our everyday lives. It starts in infancy and continues as we talk our way through changing nappies, starting the car and making a slice of toast. Keep talking, this allows children to learn about 'first', 'next', 'and then'. This brings order to language.
- As you read a story check that the child is keeping up with all

that is happening. Recap and point out the sequence of the story.

Ways to keep communication socially in tune

Children may be familiar with language but still communicate poorly. For conversation to be in tune we need to listen then respond appropriately at the right time. We must be sensitive to gesture and tone of voice, then answer in the right way. This use of effective communication in day-to-day life is referred to as the pragmatics of language, which are often weak in ADD children.

These children tend to interrupt, talk over others or answer without listening. They go off in their own direction without tuning in to the other party. They misread the social cues and barge in, soon wedging their foot well and truly in their mouths. The pragmatics are further upset as they interrogate, come on too strong, and can't keep eye contact.

- When the two-way conversation is breaking down, gently put the brakes on it: 'Wait a minute, you've lost me.' 'Can we just check that again?'
- Encourage eye contact and tell the child when it is not happening: 'Who are you talking to now?'
- Let the child know when they are being annoying or rude, but don't make a big deal of it.
- Role-play polite ways of handling situations, but take it gently and keep it light.
- Playing board and card games helps to develop turn-taking skills.
- Praise and encourage when speech is clear, appropriate and on target.
- Never become a negative nagger, who turns a happy, inappropriate speaker into an angry, obstinate mute.

- These ideas are sound in theory but in most ADD children the pragmatics are painfully slow to improve.

Ways to encourage comprehension of long instructions

ADD children are often easily distracted, quickly bored and have a poor active working memory. This severely limits the amount of information they can cope with at any one time.

- Before you start speaking gain their attention and make good eye contact.
- Structure what you say with the first things presented first.
- Keep it simple, remove unnecessary words.
- Communicate away from competing noise.
- Be specific about the messages you wish to get across. This helps the child to be specific about what we demand of them.
- Complicated information must be broken into short, easily understood chunks.
- With little children, get down to their eye level and physically hold their hands still when an important message must be transmitted.
- Use cue words to catch attention: 'Ready to listen.' 'Wait for it.'
- Be enthusiastic. Say what you mean and mean what you say.

Ways to help the child see the whole picture

When impulse control is poor many ADD children will respond rapidly to the least important, 'wrong' part of a message. This is like a quiz show contestant who hits the buzzer when only the first quarter of the question has been given. Responding without listening is particularly irritating for those who have to live with the ADD child.

- Gain eye contact, keep the environment quiet, sort out what you want to say before you say it.
- Emphasise the key words: '**Point to all** the animals in the picture that **do not** eat the grass.'
- As you read at bedtime, talk about the story, perhaps discussing other relevant topics.
- Discuss what you have just been watching on the television during the commercial breaks.
- Emphasise by action and gesture.
- Take it slowly and check that they have understood what is important before encouraging their response.

Ways to help with vague, open-ended questions

When you are somewhat inattentive, impulsive and have a poor short-term memory it is easier to work with concrete black and white information. Children with ADD find it particularly difficult to respond to questions that require reasoning, thinking, planning and drawing on past experience.

- As you go about your daily activities sometimes try to move away from questions about the here and now and approach events in a more abstract way, for example, 'When we fill the car with petrol, why does it say "no smoking" on the petrol pump?'
- As you read a story, stop before you move to the next page and ask, 'What do you think is going to happen next?'
- If the child cannot come up with their own ideas, give them some alternatives, for example, 'Do we not smoke at the

petrol pump because it is bad for your health?' 'Do we not smoke because . . .?'

- Use information from films, videos, current affairs or children's shows to talk 'around' a topic, that is, to use the topic as a basis for other discussions.

- Talk in an interested, casual manner and keep it fun.

- With all these ideas, there is a fine dividing line between encouraging good speech and annoying the stubborn child that won't talk at all.

Acknowledgment: The ideas in this chapter come from Jeanette Cowell and her Speech Pathology colleagues at Royal Alexandra Hospital for Children, Sydney.

16

Encouraging Self-esteem

ADD is a real confidence crusher. If a child struggles at school, is socially inept and in trouble all the time, it is no wonder that esteem sinks. Of course, some ADD children are so thick-skinned, that they bounce through with remarkable resilience. Then there are those who star at sport, which helps shore up their confidence. Unfortunately, for most it is a hard road they tread, but one that can be made more comfortable if we boost, not crush, confidence.

The negative spiral

Parents need to be almost super-human to remain positive and encouraging as they live with an ADD child. Certainly, at the time the diagnosis is made, many parents are already at a pretty low ebb. They blame themselves and feel failures. Others find fault in everything their child does and are now engaged in a no win war. Some start to wonder if a child is deranged, brain damaged or moving towards prison.

It is sad to see parents, who were so full of hope and enthusiasm when their children were little, now so negative and disillusioned. Even worse is the effect of these unhealthy attitudes on the child.

Children can't see themselves, they judge their self-worth from the reactions of those around them. We are the mirror that shows them how they are appreciated and through this they shape their self-image. If esteem is to remain high we must encourage, value, help and watch what we say to our children so that they will savour success.

Confidence crushers

Parents and teachers can undermine esteem, not just by the words we use, but also by the way we use them. Intonation, lack of interest, put downs and implied incompetence all take their toll. After a while, this erosion of esteem becomes so easy, we hardly know we are doing it.

Don't listen

When you live with a child who nags, complains and rabbits on, you switch off to survive. But if children are to feel valuable, what they say should be valued. When they rush in from school wanting to tell of some great adventure they need an audience, not: 'Wait until the news is over.' 'Oh yes.' Yawn!

It is not easy, but if we don't encourage communication, soon they will not try to tell us anything.

Put downs

ADD children may appear to be insensitive and irritating, but it doesn't mean they are not upset by hurtful remarks. Be particularly careful of the 'you' statements: 'You know it all, don't you?' 'You never think of anyone else.' 'You annoy me all the time.' 'You make a mess of everything.'

'You' statements are never so hurtful if turned into 'I' statements: 'I get upset when we don't get on together.' 'I find it hard work tidying up all this mess.' Remember, it is the behaviour and not the child you dislike.

Overprotect, undertrust

When you have seen the ADD child stumble into so many dangerous and stupid situations, it is natural to become overprotective. But it is hard to feel you are a competent person when parents constantly say: 'Don't climb, you know you always fall.' 'Don't slice the bread, you'll cut your finger.' 'Don't run, you will trip.' 'Don't go in the surf, you'll do something stupid.' 'Don't ride your bike, you ride too dangerously.'

There is a difficult dividing line between keeping our children safe and stifling them with overprotection. Children need to feel trusted if they are ever going to achieve independence and good self-esteem.

Comparisons

Children are unique, they don't need to be compared with

their cousins and classmates. The ADD child will not be as tidy as their brother or study like their sister, but so what? Children need to be respected for their individuality and not have their noses wiped in it. When human beings of any age try to live up to other people's inappropriate ideals, they crack and lose confidence.

Fault finding

Every one of us knows how much it hurts when we produce our best work, yet receive nothing but criticism. Children are just as sensitive: 'Look what I made.'—'Oh, what is it?' 'I got dressed all by myself today.'—'It would look better if your shirt wasn't inside out.' 'I've just washed the dishes for you.'—'There's dirt on that one, let me do it. I'll wash them properly.' When children do their best, they need to be encouraged, not undermined.

Words that wound

When we are utterly exasperated it is easy to say things we know we should never say: 'You're such a pest.' 'Can you do nothing right?' 'You know how to make everyone's life unhappy.' 'I can't trust you to do anything.' We need to get rid of words like dumb, stupid, ruin, pest. If we don't drop destructive language, it is esteem that will drop instead.

The focus on failure

There is one great difference between adults and children. Both have their individual strengths and weaknesses, but only adults are allowed to promote what they are good at and hide their problems.

Clumsy children have to front up with 30 others and be

embarrassed as they exercise. Poor readers have to expose this weakness as they read in front of the class. Children who cannot spell can't hide it with illegible writing or a good secretary.

Parents often lose sight of their children's need to savour success. All the focus seems to be on failure: 'He runs like he's impaired.' 'He can remember nothing.' 'His reading is awful.' 'He has no style to his swimming.'

It is hard enough living with parents who can only see your weaknesses, but when you struggle through school and arrive home to find an army of tutors and therapists ready to focus further on your bad points, life becomes pretty negative.

Converting to confidence

For children to feel good about themselves, they must see that their words are valued, that their talents are appreciated and that they themselves are respected and trusted. At the same time, those who care for them need to encourage esteem, and in everything the focus must move from failure towards savouring success at something.

Wonderful words

Take time to listen as the ADD child talks. Acknowledge what the child says, keep eye contact throughout the conversation and let them finish without interrupting them. Show you're interested and let them know you care. Use plenty of encouragement: 'You're great.' 'I like it.' 'Give it a go.' 'I believe in you.'

Well done

Take time to watch what they are doing, appreciate their effort and give help when it is needed. When things are not right, guide don't criticise: 'Gosh, if you tidy this a tiny bit, it will be perfect!' Look past the bad bits to see the good. For example, their writing may be messy and their spelling poor, but the story is full of talent. Let them know you are pleased: 'That's good.' 'You're right.' 'You bust yourself, but you did it.' 'That's so much better.' 'You're really improving.'

Respect and trust

Things may get spilt or broken and the work may be substandard, but at least the child is trying. Encourage them to do as much as they can without putting anyone at too much risk. Without responsibility and our trust, children feel inadequate and lack independence.

A wonderfully wise mother recently gave us her views of esteem: 'If you treat your children the way you would like to be treated yourself, you will never go far wrong.'

Confidence in the classroom

Teachers tread a tightrope. They know the ADD child needs a lot of extra attention, but they realise that esteem suffers if they are seen to stand out as different. It is quite a balancing act, particularly when the child is often unpredictable, disruptive and difficult.

School is stressful for a child with ADD. Twice the effort will achieve the same results as anyone else. Equal effort gets them nowhere. If teachers are to hold esteem and interest, they need to continually encourage the child. When attention is hard to hold, use material that is of interest. If the child is into fishing, let them read, write, talk about and count fish. If it is sport, dinosaurs or whatever, encourage their interest.

Teachers should follow the same suggestions already mentioned for home. They need to watch their choice of words, to encourage the children and to let them feel important. The ADD child may be intensely irritating, but their behaviour and self-image will be stronger if they are noticed, can share special tasks and are allowed the same privileges as would be granted to the potential Rhodes Scholar or a number one nerd in the class.

Savouring success

A life which is all failure and no fun gets pretty depressing. As parents we need to look past the problems of school, to find hobbies, interests and outside activities our children enjoy. We must move the focus from what our children cannot do to what they can do. Confident children are those who savour success at something and it is up to us to find out what that something is (see also Chapter 17 for suggestions on sport, interests and hobbies).

17

Choosing the Right Sport, Hobbies and Other Activities

At the end of the school day, the active ADD child hits the out-side world like an escaped prisoner. They want space, freedom, exercise and enjoyment. It is imperative that these school-stressed children have outside interests. It is up to parents to find what suits the child best.

Avoiding social stress

Many ADD children are uncomfortable in social situations. They look awkward, don't know what to say and feel out of place. As we plan outside interests, it is important to find ones that bring maximum enjoyment and minimal social stress.

The secret is to look for activities that give space and leave the child firmly in charge of their own communication. Those we have found most successful are hillwalking, bike riding and swimming.

In the countryside you can walk, talk, run ahead, look around then talk some more. On a bike, you can speak to a friend, do a few wheelies and speak again. At the pool or beach you can meet new friends, splash around then come back and talk some more. With activities like these they are in charge of their own communication and can avoid uncomfortable social pressure.

Another way to keep things comfortable is to ensure that they have friends with similar interests. The BMX racers, horse riders, mechanical minds and football fans don't need small talk, they can rabbit on all day. As they talk about bikes, horses and their sports heroes, it may bore us out of our brains, but in this company they are a star.

The best sports and activities
Swimming

This is our number one recommendation for ADD children. Not only is it an outlet for energy, it also provides a socially useful interest which they will still have in adulthood. These children can learn to swim safely at an early age, but it takes quite a few years to get their arms, legs and breathing synchronised in style. Many parents tell us that their children hate swimming. It is not swimming they dislike, it is the long, boring lessons which turn them off.

Swimming is not only about style, it is about enjoying yourself in the water. ADD children need less lessons and far more fun, and preferably splashing around with a parent beside them in the water.

Football and sports

Some of our ADD children are a sensation at sport and this success brings a great boost to their esteem. Others don't have the coordination or concentration to do well, but they still enjoy the outing.

Football is one of the best sports for the young ADD child, but inattention means that many go walkabout, lose interest, run in the wrong direction or drift off to pat a passing dog. Cricket works well when the team is winning, but when dismissed for a duck, most are particularly poor losers.

If they show any interest in team sports they should be encouraged. They don't need to pass like Pele or bat like Botham but if they enjoy what they are doing it does not matter how good they are.

Bicycles

ADD children are not the safest riders on the road, but for many, bikes give space, freedom and an escape from the frustrations of life. If they are old enough and the roads are relatively quiet, get them up on two wheels. After a hard day at school it is great to burn off some energy and this allows them to mix in a socially comfortable way. Many of the world's most talented mechanics were once ADD children who started by stripping and tuning their bikes.

Fishing

There is something about fishing that seems to soothe. Many of our ADD children fish from piers and rocks, and can even sit relatively still for a period of time. Some of the most active can sit quite still in a small boat. Fishing gives space and is free from social stress. If you live near water, why not give it a go?

Judo and Tae Kwan Do

Parents are reluctant to direct an impulsive, immature child into anything that might encourage violence. Certainly no one would recommend pistol shooting, knife throwing or pyrotechnics, but Judo and Tae Kwan Do are different.

These martial arts have been greatly enjoyed by many of our children. They teach organisation and anticipation, and have the right amount of interest and discipline to keep the attention of the usually inattentive.

Cubs, Scouts and other groups

About two-thirds of our ADD children seem suited to Scouts. They enjoy the activity, the practical parts and the interest in the outdoors. Some children do not fit comfortably into this structure and should be withdrawn when it starts to seem like school to them.

Athletics

Ten years ago it was fashionable to encourage clumsy children into Saturday morning athletics. This helped coordination, enhanced socialisation skills and strengthened up their muscles. But running last was never good for self-esteem.

If your child enjoys sprinting, jumping and cross-country

running that's great, but when it seems all pain and no pleasure let them give it a miss.

Cooking

Some of the world's great chefs have ADD. It is surprising how children enjoy cooking when encouraged by their parents. Some of our ADD children are immensely creative in the kitchen. Unfortunately, they are less creative when it comes to cleaning up. Cooking is an interest we often overlook. If they enjoy it, encourage it.

Hobbies, crafts and interests

The children in our care have all sorts of pastimes. We have potters, painters, football fanatics, collectors, actors, singers, music lovers, gardeners, walkers, horse riders, water skiers, woodworkers, mechanics (and thousands of television addicts).

Every ADD child has some talent just waiting to be tapped. Parents need to be on the lookout for new activities and interests all the time. We must be patient, as ADD children swing from immense enthusiasm to total turn-off in what seems like a matter of minutes. But don't give up, keep looking for new talents to encourage, which will bring enjoyment and boost the child's esteem.

Computer games

The ADD child may be unable to concentrate in class, but put some in front of a computer game and they will outplay anyone. Parents must realise that it is the game, not the computer, they like. If you slip in a remedial program their interest may evaporate. It is important for ADD children to be competent with computers, and computer games are a good way to start them off.

Conclusion

The school-stressed child needs to develop a protective shield of outside activities. These can be sports, hobbies, clubs or anything that brings enjoyment and a sense of success.

Parents must encourage these activities but not include too many lessons. It is wonderful when an ADD child stars and has perfect style, but it is more important to enjoy than to excel.

18

The Dark Side— Oppositional Defiant Disorder and Conduct Disorder

There are two potentially serious psychiatric disorders which quite frequently occur alongside ADD: Oppositional Defiant

Disorder (ODD) and Conduct Disorder (CD). These disorders are not caused by ADD, they coexist, much as dyslexia, tics or Tourette's syndrome can coexist with ADD. The ODD child is stubborn, defiant, provocative and oppositional (ie always takes the opposite view). The CD child's behaviour is socially inappropriate, aggressive and often downright delinquent.

These conditions, especially the aggressive form of CD, occur predominantly in boys. Though not caused by ADD, some believe their presentation is less severe if we treat our ADD children properly from an early age.

The exact incidence of ODD and CD is uncertain. North American clinics that attract the more major child behaviour problems, claim 60 per cent of their ADD children also have some of these ODD/CD behaviours. This appears a skewed overestimate. We believe that the Australian rate is well under 30 per cent, with the majority of these cases being of the oppositional type and quite mild.

Oppositional Defiant Disorder is the more common condition of the two. It presents at an earlier age and is generally less severe. Conduct Disorder may be relatively mild, but when major, longstanding and unchanged by all treatment it can be serious and the situation unsalvageable. When you hear of ADD children being expelled from school, in trouble with the police and involved in antisocial acts, the diagnosis is not ADD, it is this extreme form of Conduct Disorder.

ODD—the behaviours

ADD is usually going strong before the oppositional behaviours kick in around the start of school. Parents first complain of blow-ups, arguing and open defiance which are considerably worse than would be expected with ADD alone. As they get older, these children may deliberately upset others, be spiteful, vindictive, angry, resentful, touchy and obscene in their language.

The diagnosis of ODD is made using fixed criteria (see Appendix II), where only a few of these behaviours are required to diagnose a degree of the disorder. Obviously, the greater the intensity and number of behaviours, the more severe the condition.

ODD may occur alone, though frequently it extends to merge with CD. Living with an oppositional ADD child is not easy, but generally the situation can be greatly helped by the intervention of a child psychiatrist or psychologist.

CD—the behaviours

Conduct Disorder may present along a number of lines. Some children are openly aggressive in their behaviour, for example, fighting and menacing, while others' behaviour intrudes on other people's rights, such as lying, vandalism, stealing. This is further complicated by division into two groups: one who can socialise and another group who are so socially disabled they are incapable of normal mixing, preferring life alone or 'hunting in a pack'. Conduct Disorder appears to have a significant hereditary link, particularly in its aggressive, antisocial form.

A diagnosis of CD is made with the presence of as few as three behaviours from a diagnostic list (see Appendix III). As with ODD, the extent of the problem depends on the number of behaviours present, and their severity. The condition is worsened if there are major social disabilities.

The aggressive behaviours include initiating fights, hurting animals, use of weapons, and getting one's way through force. The behaviours which intrude on the basic rights of others include repeated stealing, absconding, lying, playing truant, housebreaking, fire setting and vandalism.

Many people believe that CD is just a more severe form of

ODD, and certainly the two frequently occur together. Children may have a pure form of Conduct Disorder, which usually presents in the adolescent years. It affects mostly boys, though antisocial but generally non-aggressive forms may affect girls (see Appendix XVIII: Conduct and Oppositional Defiant Disorders, Lahey, B.B.).

Treatment and outlook

Management of ODD and CD generally requires specialist psychiatric help and is outside the scope of this book. Stimulant medication has an important part to play in therapy, as it usually helps the associated problems of ADD. Some believe that it may also have a positive effect on the CD behaviours, but this is not certain.

Those with a major degree of CD which does not respond to treatment are a great concern. Where aggression and inability to socialise are predominant problems, there is an unfortunate downside to CD. These behaviours occur mostly in males and both ADD and CD carry a significant hereditary risk of bringing their problems to the next generation. These impulsive, unthinking adults may not be able to form stable relationships, but this does not stop them having children. Anyone who works with behaviourally disturbed children is all too aware of an increased chance of extreme behaviours in children who are adopted as well as those in the care of sole parents. With sole parents, mothers are often left with the difficult child of a difficult man. This may not be a politically popular statement, but unfortunately it is true.

Conclusion

Follow-up studies over the years have shown that many children with ADD do extremely poorly in life. We now realise that children with pure ADD will generally progress well, it is those who have ADD with a major degree of ODD/CD who are the ones with the less favourable future.

When oppositional and conduct problems are mild, these children usually respond well to treatment. Unfortunately, there are some with CD whose behaviours are so entrenched and antisocial, professionals are powerless to change their course. It is devastating for parents to watch while this happens. For some, home life reaches such a low ebb that techniques such as the *TOUCHLOVE* approach are required to break clear and protect the rest of the family (see Appendix XX).

When children with pure ADD are properly managed, the outlook must be viewed with great optimism. When we hear of ADD children who have gone off the rails, it is rarely ADD that is the problem, it is the associated difficulties, particularly of CD. When severe and resistant to treatment, this is definitely the dark side of ADD.

19

Adults with ADD

The idea of adult ADD is new and somewhat controversial. At the time of writing, many psychologists and psychiatrists dispute its existence and it is extremely hard for adults to find help. We see this as a common condition, which occurs in many parents of the ADD children we treat.

In the 1970s we had 'hyperactive children' who were said to get better in their primary school years. In the 1980s the ADD behaviours were said to stay through the school years, with a small number having problems continuing into adulthood. In the 1990s we believe that approximately 60 per cent of children with ADD will bring some of their symptoms with them into later life.

Today many of our most successful businesspeople, enter-tainers, entrepreneurs and prominent public people still suffer some symptoms of ADD. Most underachieved at school, but later got going, using their great energy to push through every obstacle, following the ADD pattern of early failure and late achievement. They may be highly regarded and famous, yet many of these successful people remain restless, paranoid, easily frustrated, volatile, impulsive, inattentive, weak at read-ing and socially ill at ease.

Adult ADD may not be a popular diagnosis at present, but five years from now we believe that it will be a major part of practice for those treating the emotions of adults.

The picture

When we diagnose a child with ADD it is surprising how often a parent discovers the reason for their own social, learning and behavioural weaknesses. Most of the adults we see knew nothing of ADD, they just believed they were not very clever. They struggled as children and some are still struggling. As they talk to us, they tell of problems in a number of areas, such as concentration, spelling, writing, memory, organisation, reading, restlessness, rigidity, relationships and a having a 'short fuse'.

Most of these adults have a mild presentation of ADD, but one that leaves them vulnerable and with some feelings of inadequacy. A number are driven, single-minded, successful people, but as they charge through life they can create con-siderable stress to those around them. A few are destroyed by ADD and Conduct Disorder, becoming unreliable, unem-ployable and dangerously unpredictable. Many of this latter group find it hard to maintain close relationships and have left home, often leaving sole mothers who struggle to look after their children.

The diagnosis

If adult ADD is to be considered, two factors are required. First, there must be a clear history of ADD in childhood. Second, some parts of this childhood presentation must remain.

There is no simple diagnostic test for adult ADD. The diagnosis is made when a number of ADD behaviours cause problems in relationships, learning and work. The ADD symptoms must predominate and not be overshadowed by associated conditions, such as alcoholism, personality problems and major depression.

Adult ADD—the weaknesses

These adults may have outgrown their childhood, but not their ADD. The problems that once caused stress, still cause stress. The difference with ADD in adulthood is that we have learned how to camouflage the symptoms by organising our lives around them.

Poor concentration and memory

Adults find it difficult to listen in a lecture, to remember instructions and telephone numbers. At work they shuffle papers, become side-tracked, and don't get on with the main business. With so much drive and energy, output appears good but it is poor when one takes account of the effort they expend.

ADD adults find it hard to concentrate on complicated instructions, and to attend to difficult work. With their poor short-term memory, most are forgetful and unreliable unless they run their lives with routine, reminders and lists. When studying, it is easy to become disheartened as so much of what is learnt evaporates overnight.

Disorganisation

ADD adults have difficulty planning their work and using their time wisely. Part of the problem is inattention and poor memory, but in addition most are disorganised. Their immense ADD energy gets things done, but if they only sat down, planned and set priorities, they could achieve as much with half the hassle. Disorganisation leads to poor productivity, while procrastination and poor planning sees them miss deadlines and stumble into financial strife.

Restlessness

By adulthood, overactivity has taken on a more subtle form. Now they pace, fidget, jiggle, clench their jaws and stress those they sit with. Some are on the go all the time, driven to work day and night. Many ADD adults have great bursts of busyness, punctuated by periods of remarkable inactivity, where they do nothing.

With so much pent-up energy, many ADD adults find it hard to relax while others find settling to sleep can be a particular problem.

Impulsivity—a short fuse

Acting without thought produces even more problems for adults than children. Words are said which cause conflict at work and at home. Actions are taken without proper planning and this leads to a boom/bust existence. Impulsive adults rush at things and often injure themselves. In the first years of driving, young ADD adults have four times the accident risk of their more reflective friends.

Impulsivity is frequently accompanied by inflexibility. Actions are started without proper thought and then pursued rigidly without compromise. Associated with this is also a degree of paranoia, where bystanders become blamed for all mistakes.

ADD entrepreneurs are hard to work for. They rush into new projects with great enthusiasm, then change their mind just as fast. Life in this fast lane is fast forward, fast backward, but rarely predictable.

Our work with ADD children is made much more difficult when there is an impulsive ADD parent. It is impossible to have effective discipline when a short fuse parent quibbles and escalates all the time. One of our children's behaviour was recently revolutionised when a psychiatrist successfully treated his impossible dad with Ritalin.

Reading, writing and spelling problems

Many of the ordinary battlers, high-flying businesspeople, lawyers and doctors we see have one thing in common. They pretend they are strong readers and good spellers, but they are remarkably weak for their positions in society. Specific learning disabilities may lessen with age but they rarely go away. They are so often associated with ADD it is not surprising to find them in these adults.

Despite appearances, it must never be underestimated just how much trouble residual reading, writing and spelling problems cause to these grown-ups. They hide their difficulties well, but coping with complicated print is still stressful and is avoided where possible. The fact that someone is succeeding in life doesn't mean that their specific learning weaknesses do not still cause pain.

Self-help techniques for adults with ADD

The condition of adult ADD is poorly understood by the helping professions, so most help must come from our own efforts at reorganising our lives.

Increasing organisation, attention and memory

When you're inattentive, forgetful and disorganised, you must develop an almost obsessive interest in order. It sounds difficult, but most adults who achieve have brought structure to their ADD lives by nothing more than sheer determination and self-discipline.

Organisation: Begin each day with a clear plan. You need goals, priorities and a list. Substitute structure for shambles. Carry out tasks in an ordered, step-wise way and don't move on until the work in front of you is completed. Watch the time and keep religiously to routine.

Attention: Complex tasks need to be divided into manageable chunks, as attention drifts when doing difficult work. Take a break when you have completed a task, before you address the next one. All ADD adults have good concentration times and the most demanding work should be reserved for this part of the day. ADD adults can attend but they use so much mental effort they quickly suffer brain fade. When productivity is on the wane, concentration can be recharged by getting outside, spending time at the gym, swimming or using relaxation techniques.

Memory: It is important to respond immediately or write a reminder note in a book, before the information is forgotten. Memory jogs such as knots in handkerchiefs and marks on hands may seem somewhat infantile, but they also have their place.

Information is easier to remember when tagged on to something that is already stored in the mind. When introduced to strangers called Arnold and Diana, their names can be remembered if you visualise them beside Schwarzenegger and the Princess.

Overcoming restlessness and overactivity

Adults need to be aware how their pacing, fidgeting, twitching and bull in a china shop behaviour bothers their workmates and family. Self-discipline can partly control this when in company but they must have some safety valve to release energy after hours, such as training, jogging, gardening, renovating or meditating. Nothing will turn the high energy 'hyper' into a slow-moving blob, but self-control can bring some sort of uneasy calm.

Beware of the dangerous short fuse

Unthinking actions and behavioural blow-ups are the Achilles' heel of the adult ADD. Fortunes are lost and friendships fall apart all through uncontrolled impulsivity. If you are going to succeed in life you must be on guard, particularly at those times of greatest risk, when angry, stressed or tired.

When placed under pressure, try to do nothing, rather than something stupid. Talk through options in your mind before you act. Take time when making major decisions and discuss things with a level headed friend.

Parents with a short fuse are a disaster when it comes to discipline. Before you act, stand back and see if your actions are improving or inflaming the behaviour. Many mothers tell us that their children are much better when their ADD husband is at work. You don't have to get husbands out of the house, just learn to back off when you are about to lose your self-control.

Maintaining social relationships

Many ADD adults are somewhat impulsive, intolerant, out of tune to feelings and a little paranoid. Nothing short of a miracle will change this overnight, but when aware of the difficulty, the situation can be self-helped. Try to stand back and think of the views and feelings of others. Respect their pace of doing things, rather than barging in, stirring, stressing and kicking heads. ADD children can cause great tension in a home and out of tune adults can be just as difficult.

Improving reading, writing and study

Weak readers struggle with manuals, academic articles and heavy literature. This is not all the fault of the reader, much of the blame must go on authors who present their work so poorly. Always look for literature which is well set out, interesting and cleverly written, then dump the rest.

Technical information is easier to understand if books have plenty of diagrams and illustrations. When studying, use a high-lighter pen to register the main points. Write notes as a series of headings that act as memory jogs and give structure to what's important. Weak spellers must have a dictionary at hand or move to a computer with a spell-check facility. Typing brings legibility to illegible writing and word processing allows an edit before presentation.

Adults who find reading difficult can improve with practice, but will rarely become comfortable with heavy literature. When reading is extremely difficult, books can still be enjoyed through libraries who lend out tapes of their best titles.

Professional help

Once more it must be emphasised that the idea of ADD in adults is not universally accepted and professional help may be hard to find. Before seeking treatment make sure that ADD is the main diagnosis, not one of the more serious conditions that often occur alongside ADD. If alcoholism, addiction, antisocial behaviour, violence, personality disorders or major depression are present, they must be tackled before ADD is considered.

If the behaviours described in this chapter strike a chord, try the self-help ideas we have suggested. If you want to take these further, shop around until you find a practical minded psychologist or psychiatrist who understands ADD.

A number of North American centres have shown that ADD adults can be helped by stimulant medication. The results are less dramatic than in children but there are reports of many adults whose productivity and contentment in life has been greatly improved. There is no doubt that medication does have an important place in the treatment of adult ADD, but it will be some years before our academic leaders give the approval needed for its general use.

Final thoughts

ADD is a very real condition which troubles a large number of children and adults internationally. With understanding and help, we can bring great improvements to lives, relationships, education, employment, learning and self-esteem.

Despite the current interest in ADD we see many parents who are unaware that ADD was the cause of their troubles in childhood. One of the saddest parts of our work is to meet intelligent, talented adults who still believe they are inferior, inadequate and dumb. It is criminal that this unnecessary assault on their esteem was ever allowed to take place. We can't change the past, but we can be doubly determined that the same will never happen to the ADD children of this present generation.

PART 3

Appendixes

APPENDIX I

The Criteria for Diagnosing Attention Deficit Hyperactivity Disorder (DSM–IV 1994)

A. Either (1) or (2)

1. six (or more) of the following symptoms of **inattention** have persisted for at least 6 months to a degree that is maladaptive and inconsistent with developmental level:

Inattention

(a) often fails to give close attention to details or makes careless mistakes in schoolwork, work or other activities

(b) often has difficulty sustaining attention in tasks or play activities

(c) often does not seem to listen when spoken to directly

(d) often does not follow through on instructions and fails to finish schoolwork, chores or duties in the workplace (not due to oppositional behaviour or failure to understand instructions)

(e) often has difficulty organising tasks and activities

(f) often avoids, dislikes or is reluctant to engage in tasks that require sustained mental effort (such as schoolwork or homework)

(g) often loses things necessary for tasks or activities (e.g., toys, school assignments, pencils, books or tools)

(h) is often easily distracted by extraneous stimuli

(i) is often forgetful in daily activities

2. six (or more) of the following symptoms of **hyper-activity–impulsivity** have persisted for at least 6 months to a degree that is maladaptive and inconsistent with developmental level:

Hyperactivity

(a) often fidgets with hands or feet or squirms in seat

(b) often leaves seat in classroom or in other situations in which remaining seated is expected

(c) often runs about or climbs excessively in situations in which it is inappropriate (in adolescents or adults, may be limited to subjective feelings of restlessness)

(d) often has difficulty playing or engaging in leisure activities quietly

(e) is often 'on the go' or often acts as if 'driven by a motor'

(f) often talks excessively

Impulsivity

(g) often blurts out answers before questions have been completed

(h) often has difficulty awaiting turn

(i) often interrupts or intrudes on others (e.g., butts into conversations or games)

B. Some hyperactive–impulsive or inattentive symptoms that caused impairment were present before age 7 years.

C. Some impairment from the symptoms is present in two or more settings (e.g., at school or work and at home).

D. There must be clear evidence of clinically significant impairment in social, academic or occupational functioning.

E. The symptoms do not occur exclusively during the course of a Pervasive Developmental Disorder, Schizophrenia or other Psychotic Disorder and are not better accounted for by another mental disorder (e.g., Mood Disorder, Anxiety Disorder, Dissociative Disorder or a Personality Disorder).

Code based on type:

314.01 Attention Deficit Hyperactivity Disorder, Combined Type: if both Criteria A1 and A2 are met for the past 6 months

314.00 Attention Deficit Hyperactivity Disorder, Predominantly Inattentive Type: if Criterion A1 is met but Criterion A2 is not met for the past 6 months

314.01 Attention Deficit Hyperactivity Disorder, Predominantly Hyperactive Impulsive Type: if Criterion A2 is met but Criterion A1 is not met for the past 6 months

Coding note: For individuals (especially adolescents and adults) who currently have symptoms that no longer meet full criteria, 'In Partial Remission' should be specified.

- **314.9 Attention Deficit Hyperactivity Disorder not otherwise specified**

This category is for disorders with prominent symptoms of inattention or hyperactivity–impulsivity that do not meet criteria for Attention Deficit Hyperactivity Disorder.

Reprinted with permission from the *Diagnostic and Statistical Manual of Mental Disorders*, Fourth Edition. Washington, DC. American Psychiatric Association, 1994.

APPENDIX II

The Criteria for Diagnosing Oppositional Defiant Disorder (DSM–IV 1994)

A. A pattern of negativistic, hostile and defiant behaviour lasting at least 6 months, during which four (or more) of the following are present:

(1) often loses temper

(2) often argues with adults

(3) often actively defies or refuses to comply with adults' requests or rules

(4) often deliberately annoys people

(5) often blames others for his or her mistakes or misbehaviour

(6) is often touchy or easily annoyed by others

(7) is often angry and resentful

(8) is often spiteful or vindictive

Note: Consider a criterion met only if the behaviour occurs more frequently than is typically observed in individuals of comparable age and developmental level.

B. The disturbance in behaviour causes clinically significant impairment in social, academic or occupational functioning.

C. The behaviours do not occur exclusively during the course of a Psychotic or Mood Disorder.

D. Criteria are not met for Conduct Disorder, and, if the individual is age 18 years or older, criteria are not met for Antisocial Personality Disorder.

Reprinted with permission from the *Diagnostic and Statistical Manual of Mental Disorders*, Fourth Edition. Washington, DC. American Psychiatric Association, 1994.

The Criteria for Diagnosing Conduct Disorder (DSM–IV 1994)

A. A repetitive and persistent pattern of behaviour in which the basic rights of others or major age-appropriate societal norms or rules are violated, as manifested by the presence of three (or more) of the following criteria in the past 12 months, with at least one criterion present in the past 6 months:

Aggression to people and animals

(1) often bullies, threatens or intimidates others
(2) often initiates physical fights
(3) has used a weapon that can cause serious physical harm to others (e.g., a bat, brick, broken bottle, knife, gun)
(4) has been physically cruel to people
(5) has been physically cruel to animals
(6) has stolen while confronting a victim (e.g., mugging, purse snatching, extortion, armed robbery)
(7) has forced someone into sexual activity

Destruction of property

(8) has deliberately engaged in fire setting with the intention of causing serious damage
(9) has deliberately destroyed others' property (other than by fire setting)

Deceitfulness or theft

(10) has broken into someone else's house, building or car

(11) often lies to obtain goods or favours or to avoid obligations (i.e., 'cons' others)

(12) has stolen items of nontrivial value without confronting a victim (e.g., shoplifting, but without breaking and entering; forgery)

Serious violations of rules

(13) often stays out at night despite parental prohibitions, beginning before age 13 years

(14) has run away from home overnight at least twice while living in parental or parental surrogate home (or once without returning for a lengthy period)

(15) often truant from school, beginning before age 13 years

B. The disturbance in behaviour causes clinically significant impairment in social, academic or occupational functioning.

C. If the individual is age 18 years or older, criteria are not met for Antisocial Personality Disorder.

Specify type based on age at onset:
Childhood–Onset Type: onset of at least one criterion characteristic of Conduct Disorder prior to age 10 years
Adolescent–Onset Type: absence of any criteria characteristic of Conduct Disorder prior to age 10 years

Specify severity:
Mild: few if any conduct problems in excess of those required to make the diagnosis and conduct problems cause only minor harm to others (e.g., lying, truancy, staying out after dark without permission)
Moderate: number of conduct problems and effect on others intermediate between 'mild' and 'severe' (e.g., stealing without confronting a victim, vandalism)

Severe: many conduct problems in excess of those required to make the diagnosis **or** conduct problems cause considerable harm to others (e.g., forced sex, physical cruelty, use of a weapon, stealing while confronting a victim, breaking and entering).

Reprinted with permission from the *Diagnostic and Statistical Manual of Mental Disorders*, Fourth Edition. Washington, DC. American Psychiatric Association, 1994.

APPENDIX IV

ADHD Rating Scale—Barkley and DuPaul

Child's name: _____

Age _____ Grade _____ Completed by: _____

Circle the number in the one column which best describes the child.

	Not at all	Just a little	Pretty much	Very much
1. Often fidgets or squirms in seat	0	1	2	3
2. Has difficulty remaining seated	0	1	2	3
3. Is easily distracted	0	1	2	3
4. Has difficulty awaiting turn in groups	0	1	2	3
5. Often blurts out answers to questions	0	1	2	3
6. Has difficulty following instructions	0	1	2	3
7. Has difficulty sustaining attention to tasks	0	1	2	3
8. Often shifts from one uncompleted activity to another	0	1	2	3
9. Has difficulty playing quietly	0	1	2	3
10. Often talks excessively	0	1	2	3
11. Often interrupts or intrudes on others	0	1	2	3
12. Often does not seem to listen	0	1	2	3
13. Often loses things necessary for tasks	0	1	2	3
14. Often engages in physically dangerous activities without considering consequences	0	1	2	3

Reproduced by permission from Barkley, R. A. *Attention-Deficit Hyperactivity Disorder: A Handbook for Diagnosis and Treatment*. New York, Guilford Press 1990.

APPENDIX V
Edelbrock Child Attention Problems Rating Scale

We have found this form useful in screening for the child who has major inattention but who does not have hyperactivity. Such a child is often missed by the other questionnaires which, in our experience, mainly pick up the hyperactive, impulsive ADD child.

Child's name _____

Child's age _____ Filled out by: ___ Child's sex M [ ] F [ ]

Directions: Below is a list of items that describe pupils. For each item that describes the pupil now or within the past week, check whether the item is Not True, Somewhat or sometimes true, or Very or often true. Please check all items as well as you can, even if some do not seem to apply to this pupil.

	Not true	Somewhat or sometimes true	Very or often true
1. Fails to finish things he/she starts			
2. Can't concentrate, can't pay attention for long			
3. Can't sit still, restless or hyperactive			
4. Fidgets			
5. Daydreams or gets lost in his/her thoughts			
6. Impulsive or acts without thinking			
7. Difficulty following directions			
8. Talks out of turn			
9. Messy work			
10. Inattentive, easily distracted			
11. Talks too much			
12. Fails to carry out assigned tasks			

Please feel free to write any comments about the pupil's work or behaviour in the last week.

_____

_____

_____

_____

Reproduced by permission from C. S. Edelbrock. The Pennsylvania State University. For more information see Appendix XVIII: General Reviews on ADD (Barkley, R.A.).

Tests of Persistence, Memory and Attention

The Paired Associate Learning Test

Here the examiner helps the child to learn some items of paired information. An example might be, 'In London Zoo there is an elephant, in Sydney there is a camel and in New York there is a lion.' As this information is taught, a visual stimulus is shown, e.g. a picture of a lion, and the child responds, 'New York'.

This is a test of attention, short-term memory and visual auditory learning. As it goes on, incorrect responses are put right, so that the child keeps learning all the time. The test is continued until the child achieves a perfect run or after a predetermined number of attempts.

Paired association is a demanding task which is particularly useful when studying the effects of medication. When drugs are being trialled, this test helps document the best preparation and correct dose.

The Continuous Performance Test

This is a computer task. The child sits at the keyboard watching the screen. They are instructed to press the space-bar immediately a special sequence of letters is seen on the screen. The child is scored on the number of successful targets they spot, those they miss and their reaction time.

The Continuous Performance Test has been standardised, using thousands of children both with and without ADD. This gives a reasonably objective measure of impulsivity and to a lesser extent distractibility. It is of particular value in documenting the effect or lack of effect of stimulant medication.

APPENDIX VII

Neurometrics

The standard Electroencephalograph (EEG) measures brain electrical activity. Tracings are made from electrodes placed around the skull. The resulting paper record is read by a neurologist who will note major abnormalities which suggest conditions such as epilepsy. This technique is too crude to pick up the subtle electrical differences present in ADD.

Neurometrics brings computer technology to this old EEG method. Quantitative diagnostic features are extracted from the standard EEG, cortical evoked potentials and brainstem evoked potentials to give an objective statistical evaluation of brain electrical activity. The results of this evaluation are represented by colourful maps and tables of data which highlight areas of activity that stand out as different from what would be expected for a normal child of the same age.

This technique is available for children aged six years and older. It is non-invasive, painless and unlike other scans, can cope with some movement in the restless child.

The technique

Brain waves are recorded from electrodes placed at standardised sites on the head. The electrodes are attached to a special cap which is fitted on the child. Data is collected in two main ways. Firstly, data is recorded from EEG tracings as the child sits quietly with eyes closed. Next, brainwave activity is collected whilst the child is presented with various stimuli. Flashes of light, checkerboard pattern reversals and tones or beeps are presented while measuring cortical evoked potentials. Loud clicks at 80 decibels are used while recording brainstem auditory evoked responses.

One expects to see certain patterns of response in the 'normal' child or adult. The areas where the dysfunctions occur give an indication of the anatomical and functional integrity of the brain.

In the child with ADD there is a slowing of the brainwaves which appears most prominently in the frontal regions. In children with specific reading disability certain patterns of functioning are observed which deviates from normal. Children with primarily auditory difficulties show different patterns to those with poor visual processing.

By providing a quantitative estimate of the maturational level of the brain and adequacy of information processing, one can document changes that come with medication and maturity.

Neurometrics is relatively new to the field of Paediatrics and Neurology. There are a number of clinics worldwide utilising Neurometrics in the assessment of ADD reading disability and various psychiatric disorders. This technique was first popularised in Australia by the late Dr Gordon Serfontein. He used this as an objective indicator of these imprecise conditions that were otherwise hard to document. Dr Serfontein's views were not universally accepted by his colleagues.

Current research is focusing on the use of Neurometrics in cognitive disorders, both in children and in adults. We have no doubt that Neurometrics has a place in the diagnosis and monitoring of ADD. Whether this is just another pointer towards the diagnosis or something far more specific, time will tell.

PET and SPECT Scans in ADD

For a long time researchers have tried to pinpoint the seat of ADD in the brain. Initially they used the brain wave test, electroencephalograph (EEG), but this mainly detected abnormalities in the superficial layers called the cortex and did not tap into the deeper parts. Methods such as CAT scans and MRI showed up the anatomy of the brain but in ADD there were no significant lesions. In the late 1980s new types of scan became available, which could reflect brain function. The SPECT (Single Photon Emission Computed Tomography) and PET (Positron Emission Tomography) scans look at blood flow and metabolism in different parts of the brain. This is able to indicate the areas that are being relatively over or under used.

Using Xenon-133 inhalation SPECT and [^{18}F] fluoro-2-deoxy-D-glucose PET it was found that regions located centrally and deep within the brain (called the caudate nuclei/striatum) were the most consistent areas of underfunction in ADD, as were the frontal lobes and the posterior periventricular region. In the SPECT and PET scans blood flow and glucose metabolism to these areas were low, which reflected reduced activity.

The striatum, frontal lobes and posterior periventricular region are thought to be important for controlling and directing what we attend to. As well as having complex connections with each other, these three regions are richly interconnected with the sensory cortices—the regions of the brain whose role it is to receive sensations. They act as a gate, allowing important information to register but filtering out the noise of interfering information which may prevent us from focusing on relevant messages. Because these 'filters' are underfunctioning in ADD they are unable to gate the hundreds of unimportant stimuli that arrive every minute. This constant, unchecked bombardment shows up in the sensory cortices. They become flooded with incoming messages and can be seen on the SPECT scan as high blood flow to the areas that receive vision and sound.

When Methylphenidate (Ritalin) was administered to ADD children, its effect showed up on Xenon-133 SPECT as a redistribution of blood flow in the brain. Methylphenidate appeared to increase the level of function of the under-perfused regions at the striatum, posterior periventricular region and to a lesser extent the frontal lobes. This normalisation allowed the clutter of irrelevant messages to be screened out, which could then be seen as a reduction in blood flow to the vision and hearing areas. This filtering of irrelevant distraction helps concentration.

In summary, using PET and SPECT scans we now have a way to study the function of the brain. Both have shown that in ADD there is an underfunction of those areas that screen out stimuli from the environment, that is the frontal and striatal regions. This lack of filtering shows up as excessive stimulation of the sensory receptors. These abnormalities in ADD are largely reversed by stimulants.

APPENDIX IX
Interpreting the WISC–III

This is a test of overall intelligence for children aged 6 to 16 years. The child's level of intelligence is represented by a number, called their intelligence quotient or IQ. On the Wechsler Intelligence Scale for Children–III (WISC–III), mean IQ is 100 with a standard deviation of 15. If a child is of normal intelligence, their IQ would therefore be anywhere from 85 (low average IQ) to 115 (high average IQ).

The WISC–III comprises 13 subtests, which, broadly speaking, can be divided into those which reflect verbal ability (comprising the information, comprehension, arithmetic, similarities and vocabulary subtests) and those which measure non-verbal intelligence by assessing intelligence without placing great demands on the child's language skills (comprising picture completion, picture arrangement, block design, object assembly and coding subtests). These two clusters give rise to the verbal IQ and performance IQ respectively. The remaining three subtests—digit span, mazes and symbol search—are supplementary.

Factor analysis of the WISC–III resulted in the formation of four Kaufman factors: *Verbal comprehension, perceptual organisation, processing speed* and *freedom from distractibility*. The verbal comprehension factor is computed from the information, comprehension, similarities and vocabulary subtests. The perceptual organisation factor is calculated using the picture completion, picture arrangement, object assembly and block design subtests. These derived quotients from the Kaufman factors are a 'purer' reflection of a child's verbal and non-verbal intelligence.

The speed with which a child can process information is reflected by the processing speed factor, which is derived from the coding and symbol search subtests.

The subtests arithmetic and digit span are used to form the Kaufman factor called freedom from distractibility. The freedom from distractibility factor is low in some children with ADD, but this is by no means diagnostic as performance on these three subtests is affected by reasons other than inattention.

Wechsler Intelligence Scale for Children—III

VERBAL SCORES

- + ● Information
- + ● Similarities
- ● + Arithmetic
- + ● Vocabulary
- + ● Comprehension
- × Digit span

PERFORMANCE SCORES

- ○ Picture completion
- ○ Picture arrangement
- ○ ● Block design
- ○ Object assembly
- ☆ Coding
- Mazes
- ☆ Symbol search

× Places greatest demands on ability to concentrate
● Most related to general intellectual ability
+ Best reflects the understanding and application of verbal knowledge
○ Measures the interpretation and organisation of visually presented material
☆ Requires ability to attend and to coordinate eye and hand function at speed

---

Neuropsychology Tests

These are tests of frontal lobe function used in assessing children with ADD.

The Stroop Colour-word test

This is an interference test requiring the child to filter out and inhibit competing information before responding correctly. The speed with which the child completes the test is recorded.

There are three different tasks:

1. Reading a list of colour names (red, blue and green) which are printed in black ink.

2. Naming the colour of different coloured patches.

3. Naming the colour of ink which is used to print a list of words. The words are themselves colour names which may be the same or different to the colour of ink in which they are printed.

The Trail Making test

A test of speed and of mental flexibility.

Part A: A dot-to-dot task where the child is asked to connect a series of numbered circles (1-2-3 . . .)

Part B: The child is asked to connect circled numbers alternating with circled letters of the alphabet (1-A-2-B-3 . . .)

The Wisconsin Card Sorting Test

A test of problem solving ability and of mental flexibility.

The child is required to sort a deck of cards. The cards contain geometric designs which can be sorted into different sets, according to their common features, such as shape, colour, number of squares, etc.

A computerised version is available where groups of cards to be sorted appear on the screen and the child clicks the mouse at the cards they think belong together.

ADD Lookalikes

The normal, active preschooler

The amount of activity, commonsense displayed and intensity of behaviour, varies greatly in preschoolers. Some normally active children are called overactive, but they are not ADD children. Their problem is a busy temperament which conflicts with the sometimes unreasonable expectations of their parents.

To diagnose ADD in a preschooler, the behaviours must be inappropriate even for this normally active and unthinking stage of development. Having said this, in the preschooler, ADD can be difficult to distinguish from normal, difficult temperament. Often we have thought a young child was just out of step with parental expectations and did not have ADD, but later found that ADD was the correct diagnosis. In theory this lookalike is easy to distinguish from ADD, in practice it can be quite difficult.

The hearing impaired child

When in doubt, we arrange a good preschool, give basic behaviour suggestions and see what happens over the next few months. Hopefully the diagnosis will then be clearer. Children with severe hearing loss can present with atypical behaviour, but this behaviour is often more repetitive and stereotyped than that of ADD children. Inattentive children don't listen and are often sent for hearing tests. Frequently, they are found to have a mild hearing loss caused by fluid in the middle ear (glue ear). This minor reduction in hearing does not cause ADD, but it makes life much harder for the already inattentive child. If there is ever the slightest doubt about any child's hearing, this must be formally tested. It is not known why ADD children and children with specific learning disabilities seem to have a higher incidence of glue ear.

Specific Learning Disabilities (SLD)

If children have a specific weakness in learning they become frustrated and lose concentration when the work becomes too hard. In ADD the difficult behaviours and problems of persistence are present most of the time. In children with learning disabilities these problems only occur when they are struggling with reading, mathematics, language or whatever causes them stress. In theory it should be easy to separate the behaviours of these two conditions, but as ADD and SLD regularly coexist, it is not always that simple.

Autism

This is said to be an ADD lookalike, but it would be impossible for any experienced professional to confuse the two. Autistic children are aloof, have poor verbal and body language, and are somewhat obsessive. There is one subgroup of autism where children are extremely active (the 'active but odd' subgroup). They are active but they are also extremely distant and detached. This difference makes ADD and autism like chalk and cheese.

Epilepsy

Children with epilepsy are more likely to have an associated problem of ADD. It is not the epilepsy which is causing this behaviour, it is the child's brain difference, which shows itself in two symptoms, epilepsy and ADD. Perfect control of the epilepsy rarely removes the associated problems of behaviour.

Sometimes one of the anticonvulsant medications will ex-acerbate the ADD behaviours. When in doubt, the dose or drug must be altered. Epilepsy or anticonvulsants are not a contraindication to the use of stimulant medication.

Depression

This is often said to mimic the behaviours of ADD. In our ex-perience childhood depression is quite rare and, when present, children we see usually become withdrawn, rather than over-active and impulsive. Depression, however, will frequently result from ADD. This mostly affects adolescents who become demoralised by their academic, emotional and social problems. Depression does not cause ADD, but ADD increases the risk of depression.

Intellectual disability

Parents often confuse their child's intellectual disability with ADD. If you have a five-year-old with the development of a two-and-a-half-year-old, you must expect the behaviour to be active, inattentive and unthinking, but this is not ADD.

Children with developmental delay are at increased risk of also suffering from ADD. When these two coexist, the be-haviour must be significantly out of step with the intellectual level, otherwise the diagnosis of ADD cannot be considered. Stimulant medication can be used in ADD children with in-tellectual disability, but it has less chance of success.

Brain injury

The child who has suffered some form of brain injury may pre-sent with behaviours which are difficult to distinguish from ADD. Here the quality of the behaviours is generally different, with the child tending to be more restless, agitated, learning disabled and lacking in forethought and sense.

We often see children whose parents believe that a relatively minor illness or accident has resulted in the child acquiring ADD. For a head injury to cause such behaviour there would usually be a prolonged period of unconsciousness and weeks in hospital. For a medical condition (for example, meningitis or encephalitis) to cause these symptoms the child will generally have been critically ill.

When ADD is the diagnosis, there will be a gradual onset. With a brain injury, there is a dramatic change in personality, learning and behaviour immediately following the traumatic event.

Behaviours that are caused by brain injury are managed in very much the same way as those of ADD, though stimulant medication is less successful.

Family dysfunction

Though authors rarely consider this aspect at length, we find the unclear blend of inborn ADD and the behaviours associated with a disturbed home environment, to be the most difficult differential in diagnosis. Stress, inconsistency and emotional disadvantage cause major problems of behaviour to any child. These problems are usually different from pure ADD, the children being more attention-seeking, defiant and unmanageable, though there is some overlap.

The confusion comes as the statistics show ADD behaviour to be more common in disadvantaged families. It is easy to blame it all on poor parenting, but it is not as simple as that. The adults in dysfunctional families sometimes slip to their disadvantaged situation through their academic under-achievement and their impulsive, disorganised, socially inept behaviour. The children of such relationships are then more likely to inherit the ADD genes from one or both parents. Now we have a child with the predisposition to ADD who will be made many times worse by the inconsistent management of a volatile home. The presence of family dysfunction does not exclude ADD, the two can coexist. Often it is easier to treat ADD than dysfunction.

ADD in association with major family problems will greatly increase the risk of the associated condition, conduct disorder (CD). Here the unthinking innocent behaviour of ADD changes to become deliberate and downright aggressive. This is a serious scenario, one that is often hard to change. If ADD is part of the problem and stimulant medication is effective, this often brings some improvement to an otherwise no win situation.

The Non-stimulant Medications

Clonidine (Catapres)

This is particularly useful in the overactive, impulsive, aggressive child who is not adequately controlled on stimulants alone. This drug has little effect on inattention and distractibility. For this reason Clonidine and stimulants are often prescribed in combination.

Clonidine can be given on its own to ADD children who are unable to tolerate stimulants due to tics or Tourette's syndrome. It is also said to have a place in treating the over-focused, perseverative child.

Some suggest Clonidine as the first choice for the preschooler with difficult behaviours with stimulants being added, to help attention, at the start of school. Most see it as a second line drug for the preschooler and third line in the older child (behind stimulants and antidepressants).

Action

Most behavioural benefits are seen in the first four to six hours though clinical improvement can last up to 12 hours. Adverse sedative effects are common in the early days of prescribing; these occur mostly in the first one and a half hours after taking the tablet. It may take up to two weeks to see a positive response and two months for the effect to hit its full peak.

Side-effects

Sedation is the greatest problem and though this usually eases after three weeks, in about 10 per cent of children, these sedative side-effects make drug therapy untenable. Other children feel confused, while some have headaches or suffer aggressive outbursts. Hypotension is possible, but it does not seem to be a significant side-effect when the child is otherwise healthy at the relatively low ADD levels. Hypoglycaemia is another theoretical side-effect, and to protect against this, Clonidine should be taken with food. Depression has been noted in some Clonidine-treated children, but it is probable that this only occurs in those who are already depressed.

It is important to remember that Clonidine does effect blood pressure and cardiac output, also there have been reports of occasional alterations of heart rhythm in adults. **Parents must be made aware that exceeding the prescribed dose can be dangerous.** When Clonidine treatment is stopped this should be tailed off gradually over several weeks.

With so much anti-stimulant propaganda over the years less restricted drugs such as Clonidine have been seen as relatively safe. We urge caution. Clonidine may not be a scheduled drug, but it is not without its problems.

The response

Though our experience is less favourable, some colleagues state that 70 per cent of their overactive, impulsive children respond well to Clonidine. Parents usually see greater benefits than teachers as Clonidine is more likely to improve compliance, which is particularly helpful for parents. Teachers are more interested in distractibility and inattention and these may remain unaltered. Measurement of Clonidine levels in the blood is unreliable and is not recommended.

Imipramine (Tofranil)

Imipramine (Tofranil), Desipramine (Pertofran) and Amitryptilline (Tryptanol) are the tricyclic antidepressants used to treat children with ADD. Most experience is with Tofranil and only this preparation will be discussed in detail. The antidepressants are less effective than the stimulants. They have been found to decrease restlessness, impulsivity and anxiety while to some extent increasing attention span. They may have no direct effect on memory, learning, aggression or the symptoms of Conduct Disorder. The tricyclics are prescribed when stimulants have failed or cannot be used because of contraindications. Most review papers state that they can be given when tics are present. A few doctors question this advice as they believe Tofranil can stir up tics and the symptoms of Tourette's syndrome. The tricyclics are also used when depression appears to be associated with ADD.

Action

The antidepressant Tofranil has a much longer action than the stimulants, its half-life is between 10 to 20 hours and it may be given once or twice daily. The dose given in ADD is usually lower than when using the drug to treat depression and the effect appears sooner. Minor benefits are occasionally reported in a matter of hours with significant gain coming in one to two days.

Children can become tolerant to Tofranil and when the effect lessens the dose may be increased once, but after this it is best to move to another medication.

To prescribe

As a rule of thumb, in children under eight years start at 10 mg at night and increase at two-weekly intervals by 10 mg increments, to reach a dose of 20 mg or 30 mg per day. Older children can be started with 10 mg or 25 mg and increased at either 10 mg or 25 mg increments up to 100 mg per day. This is usually given in two separate doses per day, though occasionally more doses are suggested to provide even levels in the sensitive child.

The review literature suggests a dose between 1 mg and 4 mg/kg/day, but we believe it is best to keep the dose under 2.5 mg/kg/day. Conservative colleagues give the child under 30 kg one 10 mg tablet twice a day (7.30 am and 3.30 pm). The older child gets the tablets at (7.30 am, 3.30 pm and bedtime) and the adolescent gets a slightly larger dose.

Side-effects

Sedation is a common side-effect of the antidepressants and is usually noted soon after starting treatment. This is initially felt in the morning as an after-effect of the evening tablet. Sleepiness usually eases with continuation of treatment but can recur with each increase in dosage.

Other side-effects are usually associated with high doses and include dry mouth, constipation, blurred vision, and even urinary retention. Tics may be worsened and some children can become confused and emotionally upset. Sudden cessation of treatment with the tricyclic antidepressants can cause a flu-like withdrawal syndrome, with nausea, vomiting, headache, lethargy and irritability. These problems can be prevented by slowly tapering off the drug over several weeks.

On extremely rare occasions heart rate and blood pressure can be significantly altered. There is also a very small print concern about problems of heart conduction. There have been several unexplained deaths in prepubertal children on Pertofran (Desipramine), as well as one death on Tofranil in the last

20 years. It must be emphasised that there have been hundreds of thousands of children treated with these drugs and this is an extremely unlikely possibility, but it is always in the back of the prescribing doctor's mind. Imipramine is metabolised in the body to Desipramine which means that both these preparations have a potential risk. Monitoring plasma levels has been recommended at the higher dosages. Some doctors perform a routine Electrocardiograph (ECG), but this is probably more effective in protecting doctors from the legal profession than children from heart problems.

Before parents panic, let's put the risks into perspective. Impulsive, unthinking children with untreated ADD are accident-prone. Each has an increased risk of serious injury. For one child with side-effects, thousands are saved painful injuries and will remain alive. Nothing in this world is 100 per cent safe; we need to take a balanced view.

Note: The antidepressants may not be dispensed with the same restrictions as the stimulants, but they are extremely dangerous when an overdose is accidentally ingested by the ADD child or their young siblings. Store antidepressants with care.

APPENDIX XIII
The Stimulant Medications—Small Print Side-Effects

Every drug has the potential to cause side-effects in some people. The common problems associated with stimulants are covered in Chapter 11. Some of the less common side-effects:

Stomach aches

Nausea

Dizziness

Strange feelings and fears

Drowsiness

Nail biting

Talks less

Talks more

Overfocused

Perseverative–obsessional

Minor increases in heart rate and blood pressure

Lowered convulsive threshold

Psychosis (at the high dose—reversible)

If you are ever concerned about a significant side-effect, the stimulants must be stopped immediately and the prescribing doctor contacted. Almost every action we take in life has some degree of calculated risk and we must always ensure that the benefits greatly outweigh any possible danger.

Those who can only see the small print possibilities forget that undertreatment of ADD also has major side-effects. Family relationships may be ruined and a child's self-esteem destroyed. There is a greater chance of becoming a dropout and involved in behaviour that is dangerous to themselves or society. Nothing in life is 100 per cent safe, but let's keep things in perspective.

APPENDIX XIV

The Original Feingold K–P Diet for Hyperactivity (1975)

Dr Feingold divided foods into two groups. Group 1 were those which contained natural salicylates. Group 2 was made up of all those which had artificial flavour or colour added.

A diary should be kept which outlines all food in the diet. When there is any change in behaviour, check the diary to see what dietary infraction has occurred. All package and container labels should be carefully checked. Practically all candies (lollies) and ice-creams on the market have artificial colours and flavours and should be avoided. Feingold suggested candies, ice-cream and sweet food should all be prepared at home.

The greatest success is observed when the entire family adheres to the diet and prohibited foods are kept out of the house. The diet must be adhered to 100 per cent as any less will lead to failure. Often a single bite or a single drink could cause an undesired response which may persist for 72 hours or more. Two infractions a week can keep a child in a persistent state of disturbed behaviour.

On the average a good response would be observed within 7 to 21 days of commencing the diet. In some children a favourable response will be noted as early as the first week, but sometimes as late as 7 weeks.

Diet

	Not Permitted	Permitted
Fruits	Almonds. Apples. Apricots. Blackberries. Gooseberries. Raspberries. Strawberries. Cherries. Currants, Grapes, Raisins or any product made from grapes, including Wine, Vinegar, Jellies, etc. Nectarines. Oranges. Peaches. Plums. Prunes. Tomatoes and all tomato products. Cucumbers and Cucumber Pickles.	Pears, Pineapples and fruits which are not on the Not Permitted list.
Cereals	All cereals with artificial colours and flavours. All instant breakfast preparations.	Any cereal without artificial colours or flavours, dry or cooked.
Bakery Goods	All manufactured cakes, cookies, pastries, sweet rolls, doughnuts, etc. Pie crusts, frozen baked goods, many packaged baking mixtures.	Any product without artificial colour or flavour. All commercial breads except egg bread and whole wheat (usually dyed). All flours. Most non-bread bakery items must be prepared at home.
Meats	Salami. Frankfurts. Sausages. Meat-loaf. Ham. Bacon. Pork.	All fresh meats.
Poultry	All barbequed types. All self-basting and pre-stuffed turkeys.	All poultry except stuffed.
Fish	Frozen fish fillets that are dyed or flavoured. Fish sticks that are dyed or flavoured.	All fresh fish.

	Not Permitted	Permitted
Desserts	Manufactured ice-creams unless the label specifies no synthetic colouring or flavouring. The same applies to ices, gelatines, junkets and puddings. Flavoured yoghurt, all dessert mixes.	Homemade ice-cream without artificial colouring or flavouring. Gelatines which are homemade from pure gelatine and contain only permitted natural fruit or fruit juices. Tapioca. Homemade custards and puddings. Plain yoghurt.
Candies	All manufactured types, hard or soft.	Homemade candies without almonds.
Beverages	Cider. Wine. Beer. Diet drinks. Soft drinks. All instant breakfast drinks. All quick mix powdered drinks. Tea, hot or cold. Prepared chocolate milk.	Grapefruit juice. Pineapple juice. Pear nectar. Guava nectar. Homemade lemonade or limeade (from fresh lemons or limes). 7UP. Milk.
Miscellaneous items	Margarine. Coloured butter. Mustard. All mint flavoured items. Soy sauce if flavoured or coloured. Cider vinegar. Wine vinegar. Commercial chocolate syrup. Barbecue flavoured potato crisps. Cloves. Ketchup (tomato sauce). Chilli sauce. Coloured cheeses. Aspirin. Mouthwashes. Cough drops. Throat lozenges. Antacid tablets. Perfumes. All toothpastes and tooth-powder. (Note): A salt and soda mixture can be used for cleaning teeth.	All cooking oils and fats. Sweet butter (not coloured or flavoured). Mustard prepared at home from pure powder and distilled vinegar. Jams and jellies made from permitted fruits which are not artificially coloured or flavoured. Honey. Homemade mayonnaise. Distilled white vinegar. Homemade chocolate syrup. All natural white cheeses.

From *Why your child is hyperactive*—Feingold B.F. Random House, New York, 1975.

APPENDIX XV
Modern Attitudes Towards Diet

The foods we now eat have been selected using trial and error over thousands of years. As we all are different in our sensitivities, it is no surprise that many people are intolerant to some foods.

Food allergy vs food intolerance

When the body reacts to a protein in food, this is called a food allergy. When sensitive to some of the chemical constituents, this is food intolerance. *Food allergies* are more frequent in infants and young children, particularly those who suffer eczema. The most common problems come from proteins in eggs, cow's milk and peanuts, though others may also cause difficulties.

Allergy typically presents with an immediate local reaction around the mouth, sometimes followed by vomiting, hives, swelling, breathing difficulties and even shock. With allergic reactions, antibodies are found in the blood and the offending protein can be isolated by a skin prick test (a series of possible products placed on the forearm, the skin surface broken and a local reaction noted when there is allergy).

Food intolerance is a much less clear-cut condition. Many foods may be involved, the response is dose-related and frequently cumulative. A little of the offending product may be taken from one food, more from another and finally the body is tipped over the edge by eating some from a totally different source. This makes intolerance hard to diagnose as the food that tips the balance may not be the main culprit. The reaction may be to one or a number of chemicals, either natural or added.

The timing of reactions can be anywhere from 30 minutes up

to 24 hours or more after eating a problem food. Where behaviour is affected by diet, this is generally due to food chemical intolerance, not allergy.

The symptoms of intolerance can include irritability, tenseness, out of control or out of character behaviour, overactivity, headaches, abdominal discomfort, mouth ulcers, irritable bowel symptoms, rhinitis, leg cramps and recurrent hives. Symptoms can occur in isolation or in any combination. The possibility of intolerance is much higher when there is a significant family history of similar symptoms. Diagnosis of intolerance can only be made by a carefully monitored elimination diet followed by selective challenges to isolate the problem foods. Food sensitivity is highly individual and no one diet is suitable for every child.

Food intolerance—four problem areas

Salicylates

These are a family of plant chemicals found naturally in many fruits, vegetables, nuts, herbs and spices, jams, honey, yeast extracts, tea and coffee, juices, beer and wines. They are also present in flavourings (such as peppermint), perfumes, scented toiletries, eucalyptus oils and some medications, such as aspirin, which is a member of the salicylate family.

Amines

These come from protein breakdown or fermentation. Large amounts are present in cheese, chocolate, wines, beer, yeast extracts and fish products. They are also found in certain fruits and vegetables, for example bananas, avocados, tomatoes and broad beans.

MSG (monosodium glutamate)

Glutamate is a building block of all proteins and is found naturally in most foods. In its free-form (not linked to protein) it enhances the flavour of foods. This is why foods rich in natural MSG are used in many meals, for example tomatoes, cheeses, mushrooms, stock cubes, sauces, meat extracts and yeast extracts. Pure MSG can also be used as an additive to increase the flavour of soups, sauces, Asian cooking and snack-foods.

Food additives

People who are sensitive to natural food chemicals are usually also sensitive to one or more of the common food additives. These are either preservatives which are used to keep foods fresh or colourings which are added to make foods look more attractive. The ones most likely to cause reactions are:

Colours

Artificial	102, 107, 110, 122 to 129, 133, 142, 151, 155
Natural (annatto)	160b

Preservatives

Sorbates	200 to 203
Benzoates	210 to 213
Sulphites	220 to 228
Nitrates, nitrites	249 to 252
Propionates	280 to 283
Antioxidants	310 to 321

Flavour Enhancer

Monosodium glutamate   621

Most other additives are unlikely to cause reactions, for example anti-caking agents, bleaches, emulsifiers, mineral salts, propellants, food acids, sweeteners, thickening agents, vegetable gums and vitamins.

A simplified guide to diet

Doctors and dietitians who specialise in the area of diet and behaviour claim much greater success than is accepted by the general medical population. They believe that others fail through a misunderstanding of the correct way to create an individual elimination diet and challenges which are inappropriate.

The list that follows is given as a guide. It should be supervised by a specialist in diet. In the initial weeks it is often suggested that milk and wheat be also eliminated. They will be the first to be reintroduced after the elimination phase.

The diet should be followed strictly for two to six weeks. Challenges may commence after five symptom-free days. If there is no improvement in four weeks, contact your dietitian. If six weeks have passed without change, diet is unlikely to be the answer.

Food chemicals in vegetables

Low: Brussels sprouts, cabbage, celery, chives, dried beans, dried peas, green beans, leeks, lentils, iceberg lettuce, parsley, white peeled potato, shallots.

Very high: Broad beans, cauliflower, eggplant, gherkin, olive, broccoli, mushroom, spinach, tomato.

Food chemicals in fruit

Low: Pear (ripe, peeled), pear (canned in sugar syrup).

Very high: Avocado, date, grapefruit, kiwi-fruit, mandarin, orange, passionfruit, pineapple, raspberry, tangelo, grape, plum, prune, raisin, sultana, tomato.

Note: Salicylates are highest in unripe fruit and this decreases with ripening. Amines increase with ripening in fruits that go mushy, for example banana and avocado. Much of the natural chemical is close to the skin, which is why we suggest pears be peeled.

Food chemicals in meat, chicken, fish and eggs

Low: Beef, chicken (fresh, no skin), fish (fresh white), eggs, lamb, rabbit, veal.

Very high amines: Anchovies, fish roe, dried, pickled, salted, smoked fish, smoked meat and chicken, canned tuna.

Very high salicylates, amines and MSG: Meat pies, salami, sausages, seasoned meats and chicken.

Note: Browning meat, grilling or charring will increase natural amine levels.

Food chemicals in dairy foods and soy products

Low: Butter, cream, fresh cheeses, milk, plain whole milk yoghurt, soy milk.

Very high: All tasty cheeses, soy sauce.

Food chemicals in drinks

Low: Water, carob powder, milk, soy milk, decaffeinated coffee, unpreserved lemonade (not more than a glass/week).

Very high salicylates only: Cordials and soft fruit-flavoured drinks, tea, peppermint tea.

High amines only: Cocoa powder, chocolate flavoured drinks.

High salicylates and amines: Cola drinks, orange juice, tomato juice, vegetable juice.

Food chemicals in herbs, spices and condiments

Low: Chives, garlic, parsley, poppy seeds, saffron, sea salt, shallots, vanilla.

Very high: Meat extracts, soy paste, soy sauce, vinegar, tandoori, gravies, pastes (fish, meat, tomato), all sauces, stock cubes, tomato sauce, yeast extracts.

Food chemicals in cereals, grains and flours

Low: Arrowroot, barley, buckwheat, cornflour, malt, rice, rice flour, rice cereals (plain), rolled oats, sago, soy flour, rye flour, wheat, wheat flour, wheat cereals (plain).

High salicylates only: Corn flakes, cornmeal, breakfast cereals with honey.

High amines only: Breakfast cereals with cocoa.

High salicylates and amines: Cereals with fruit, nuts and coconut.

Food chemicals in jams, spreads, sugars and sweets

Low: Golden Syrup, sugar, toffee, caramels, carob, malt extract.

Very high salicylates: Honey, jams, licorice, mint-flavoured sweets, peppermints, chewing gum, fruit-flavoured sweets and ices.

Very high amines only: Chocolate (all), cocoa.

Food chemicals in fats and oils

Low: Butter, ghee, margarine (unpreserved, no antioxidant), safflower oil (no antioxidant), sunflower oil (no antioxidant).

High: Coconut oil, copha, olive oil, sesame oil, walnut oil.

Food chemicals in nuts, snacks and crisps

Low: Cashews (raw, up to 10/day), plain potato crisps.

Very high salicylates only: Fruit flavours, honey flavours, muesli bars.

Note: Cheese flavours have high levels of amines and MSG; spicy flavours have high levels of salicylates, amines and MSG.

Toiletries

Allowed: Unflavoured toothpaste, plain lightly perfumed soaps, shampoos and moisturisers; sunscreen without PABA; unscented roll-on deodorants; unscented laundry detergents and soap powders.

Avoid: Flavoured, coloured toothpaste; mouthwashes; strongly perfumed products; perfumes; after shave lotions; aerosol deodorants and hair sprays; sunscreen with PABA; fabric conditioners; washing and ironing sprays.

Challenges

Once behaviour has improved with diet, that is just the first step. Challenges are needed before the offending food or foods can be isolated.

After five consecutive symptom-free days, milk and wheat are reintroduced, if they have been removed from the elimination diet. Following this, the dietitian advises on the order of the challenges. Usually salicylates are top of the list followed by amines, MSG, Propionates (Code 280, 283), Sorbates (200, 203), etc.

It can take up to 48 hours before there is any reaction so it is important to be patient, otherwise all the effort can be lost. Three symptom-free days must be allowed before moving to the next challenge. The eventual aim is to provide an individual diet tailored for the particular child, which gives the maximum benefit for the least restrictions.

Acknowledgment: The information in this section comes from the work of Dr Anne Swain, Dr Velencia Soutter and Dr Robert Loblay of the Allergy Unit, Royal Prince Alfred Hospital, Sydney. This group and their publications act as a resource to dietitians around Australia.

The Food Lists are an extract from their comprehensive book, *Friendly Food: the Complete Guide to Avoiding Allergies, Additives and Problem Chemicals,* Murdoch Books, 1991. (Distributed by Gordon and Gotch, 68 Kingsgrove Road, Belmore NSW 2192.)

APPENDIX XVI

Practical Ways to Help Handwriting

Proficient handwriting is not a skill that comes easily to the ADD child, so be patient. Aim for legibility and content, not calligraphy. Spend short periods practising these ideas with the child, and keep it positive and fun.

Check posture

Make sure the child is sitting in a chair that supports their back. The table must not be too high or too low as this results in tense shoulders and slouched posture. Elbows should rest comfortably on the table and feet should be placed flat on the floor. It helps if the child leans slightly onto the non-writing arm, as this stabilises the paper and allows the writing arm to move freely across the page.

Check pencil grip

Some children develop a tense, awkward pencil hold which slows down written work and tires the fingers. A thicker pencil or special plastic grip can help to reduce this tension.

Circular movements

Ask the child to practise anticlockwise and clockwise circular patterns across the page. Use a large sheet of unlined paper working from left to right then repeat the drawings using paper with widely spaced lines. Eventually introduce the lined paper that is used at school.

Individual letters

Start the child drawing letters which are formed in an anti-clockwise movement—a,o,c,e,s,d,g,q—and then move on to the clockwise letters—r,n,m,h,k,b,p. Now string together a continuous row of 'n's' and 'u's'.

Curvy letters

Now the child should move on to letters drawn with a 'curvy' movement—v,w,y. Check the child's sitting posture at the table and pencil grip as you go. Praise and keep them practising. If teachers are still concerned with the quality of handwriting, ask an occupational therapist for help. Stimulant medication often brings a marked improvement to the quality of written work, particularly in the primary school age group.

Note: These ideas come from Neralie Cocks, Occupational Therapist, the Child Development Unit, Royal Alexandra Hospital for Children, Sydney, and author of the book *Skipping Not Tripping: How to help children who seem clumsy and un-coordinated*, Simon & Schuster Australia, 1993.

APPENDIX XVII

Practical Ways to Help Coordination

Children with coordination difficulty will often have problems swinging a bat, throwing and catching balls, tying shoelaces, riding a bike, running with style and assembling things with their hands. When children see themselves as clumsy they can lose confidence in themselves, and when playing with other children they can be made to feel on the 'outer'.

Parents can help to some extent, but no amount of practice will turn the poorly coordinated child into a top tennis player, football legend or star of the ballet. To help, take the pressure off them and avoid competitive sports, unless they enjoy them. Here are a few simple suggestions which should be followed in a fun way.

Throwing and catching

Throwing can be practised by aiming at a large target, such as a rubbish bin, gradually decreasing the size to an empty milk carton. With catching, arms can't coordinate quickly enough to trap the ball. Practice with a large ball, such as an inflatable beach ball, gradually working down until the child can bounce, throw and catch a tennis ball with reasonable reliability.

Hand movements

Manipulation can be improved through simple activities, such as paper weaving, threading paper clips and clay work. Construction sets should be encouraged, starting with large pieces and working towards those that are smaller. Simple craft suggestions help coordination, such as putting nails in a piece of wood and weaving string designs. Have a desk area set up with coloured felt pens and reams of paper permanently on hand.

Bicycle riding

Some children find it hard to master a two-wheeler bike. They go quite well until the move from trainer wheels and after this it is hard work. Find an open space where steering will be unimportant, and the surface not too tricky. After this there are no short-cuts, it takes hours of running behind with parents holding lightly to the saddle. If this gets too hard put the bike away for a few months and then try again.

Swimming

ADD children find it easy to kick and easy to move their arms but extremely difficult to kick, move arms and breathe all at the same time. Be reassured—all these children will become proficient swimmers, as long as we don't turn them off water while they are learning.

Swimming lessons that involve a lot of sitting around waiting to participate, generally fail. A teacher who insists on perfect style rather than safe swimming may also be unsuccessful. Most ADD children do best splashing around the pool having fun with a parent. This is better than a whole academy of swimming instructors.

Computer Programs

Computer games are one of those activities that will hold the fascination of the ADD child. Computerised education used not to be quite the same thing, but major milestones have been reached.

Note: Many of these ideas come from Neralie Cocks, Occupational Therapist, the Child Development Unit, Royal Alexandra Hospital for Children, Sydney, and author of the book *Skipping Not Tripping: How to help children who seem clumsy and uncoordinated*, Simon & Schuster Australia, 1993.

APPENDIX XVIII

The Latest Research Literature — Abstracts From the Most Important Papers and Books

General reviews on ADD

Kelly, D.P., Aylward, G.P. 'Attention deficit in school-aged children and adolescents: Current issues and practice,' *Pediatric Clinics of North America* 1992; 39:487–512.

Rostain, A.L. 'Attention deficit disorders in children and adolescents,' *Pediatric Clinics of North America* 1991; 38:607–635. *Two good general reviews on ADD.*

Barkley, R.A. *Attention Deficit Hyperactivity Disorder — A handbook for diagnosis and treatment,* New York, Guilford Press, 1990.
A comprehensive, well researched overview of the subject. Useful, interesting and highly recommended for those with an academic interest in ADD.

Voeller, K.K.S. 'Clinical management of Attention Deficit Hyperactivity Disorder,' *Journal of Child Neurology* 1991; 6: S51–S67.
Reviews current approaches to the diagnosis and management of ADD for the physician.

Rosenberger, P.B. 'Attention deficit,' *Pediatric Neurology* 1991; 7:397–405.
Focuses on the neuropsychological testing and neurobiology of ADD.

Levine, M.D. 'Attention deficits: The diverse effects of weak control systems in childhood,' *Pediatric Annals* 1987; 16:117–130.
Includes Dr Levine's unique description of the observed

behaviours and cognitive symptoms in ADD children which are incorporated into an inventory of symptoms, patented to form the ANSER system questionnaires.

Serfontein, G.L. 'An approach to attention deficit disorder,' *Modern Medicine* October 1991: 103–114.
Contains simplified diagrams of brain stem evoked potential and brain mapping of quantitative EEG and cortical visual evoked potentials to indicate the main changes in children with ADD.

Jarman, F.C. 'Management of hyperactivity: Multi-modal interventions offer best prospects'. *Current Therapeutics* August 1992; 31–39.
Stresses that medication, behaviour modification and educational interventions are of greatest value while cognitive behaviour therapy and diets are of limited benefit.

Leffert, N., Susman, A. 'Attention deficit hyperactivity disorder in children,' *Current Opinion in Pediatrics* 1993;
5:429–433.
Focuses on neuroanatomic and genetic linkages, and the effects of medication on school performance, achievement and social relationships.

The Diagnosis of ADD

Blondis, T.A., Accardo, P.J., Snow, J.H. 'Measures of attention deficit. Part 1: Questionnaires,' *Clinical Pediatrics* 1989;
28:222–228.
Looks at questionnaires which may be used to supplement office evaluation of hyperactivity noting that most have deficiencies.

Blondis, T.A., Accardo, P.J., Snow, J.H. 'Measures of attention deficit. Part 2: Clinical perspectives and test interpretation,' *Clinical pediatrics* 1989; 28:268–276.
Discusses that difficulties in the interpretation of psychological

testing arise from the significant overlap between attention defi-cit disorder and associated learning disabilities.

Sleator, E.K., Ullmann, R.K. 'Can the physician diagnose hyp-eractivity in the office?' *Pediatrics* 1981; 67:13–17.
The study emphasises the importance of historical information gathered from parents together with teacher reports as reliable aids in the diagnostic process. 80 per cent of children sub-sequently diagnosed to be hyperactive showed exemplary behaviour in the office.

Adult/Adolescent ADD

Lie, N. 'Follow-ups of children with Attention Deficit Hyp-eractivity Disorder,' *Acta Psychiatrica Scandinavia* 1991; 85:Suppl 4–40.
Comprehensive review of follow-up findings in adolescents and adults who were previously diagnosed with childhood ADD. It finds that pure ADD without conduct disorder has a good prog-nosis in relation to psychopathology, antisocial behaviour, alcohol and illicit drug abuse, education and occupation.

Silver, L.B. 'Diagnosis of attention-deficit hyperactivity dis-order in adult life,' *Child and Adolescent Psychiatric Clinics of North America* 1992; 1:325–334.
Considers the dilemma which faces the physician in making the diagnosis of ADD previously undiagnosed when first presented to the clinician in adulthood.

Bellak, L., Black, R.B. 'Attention-deficit hyperactivity disorder in adults,' *Clinical Therapeutics* 1992; 14:138–147.
An overview and suggestions for the diagnosis and management of adult ADD.

Mannuzza, S., Klein, R.G., Bessler, A., et al. 'Adult outcome of hyperactive boys: Educational achievement, occupational rank, and psychiatric status,' *Archives of General Psychiatry* 1993; 50:656–576.

Concludes that childhood ADD predicts antisocial and drug abuse disorders but not mood or anxiety disorders. A major criticism of this study is that the co-occurrence of conduct disorder was not addressed systemically and prospectively.

Ward, M.F., Wender, P.H., Reimherr, F.W. 'The Wender Utah Rating Scale: An aid in the retrospective diagnosis of childhood attention deficit hyperactivity disorder,' *American Journal of Psychiatry* 1993; 150:885–890.

An attempt to develop a new diagnostic instrument for adults to describe their own childhood behaviour, so aiding in the retrospective diagnosis of childhood ADD.

ADD with hyperactivity versus ADD without hyperactivity

Hynd, G.W., Lorys, A.R., Semrud-Clikeman, M., et al. 'Attention deficit disorder without hyperactivity: A distinct behavioural and neurocognitive syndrome,' *Journal of Child Neurology* 1991; 6:S35–S41.

Describes the entity of ADD without hyperactivity: how it differs academically and behaviourally from ADD with hyperactivity.

Cantwell, D.P., Baker, L. 'Attention deficit disorder with and without hyperactivity: A review and comparison of matched groups,' *Journal of the American Academy of Child and Adolescent Psychiatry* 1992; 31:432–438.

Describes ADD with hyperactivity as more impulsive, distractible, aggressive and suffering greater peer rejection than ADD without hyperactivity. The latter are found to have an increased incidence of learning disorder, pure language disorder, depression and 'sluggish' tempo.

Girls with ADD

Berry, C.A., Shaywitz, S.E., Shaywitz, B.A. 'Girls with attention deficit disorder: A silent minority? A report on behavioural and cognitive characteristics,' *Pediatrics* 1985; 76:801–809.
ADD in girls was associated with more severe cognitive and language deficits and greater social liability. ADD without hyperactivity in girls is even more likely to be missed than the equivalent in boys.

Drugs used in the management of ADD

Fox, A.M., Rieder, M.J. 'Risks and benefits of drugs used in the management of the hyperactive child,' *Drug Safety* 1993; 9:38–50.
A detailed look at stimulants and antidepressants.

Gadow, K.D. 'Pediatric psychopharmacotherapy: A review of recent research,' *Journal of Child Psychology and Psychiatry* 1992; 33:153–195.
Focuses on recent developments in drug therapy for childhood disorders including attention deficit disorder and learning disability.

Hunt, R.D., Capper, L., O'Connell, P. 'Clonidine in Child and Adolescent Psychiatry,' *Journal of Child and Adolescent Psychopharmacology* 1992; 1:87–102.

The stimulants

Stevenson, R.D., Wolraich, M.L. 'Stimulant medication therapy in the treatment of children with attention deficit hyperactivity disorder,' *Pediatric Clinics of North America* 1989; 36:1183–97.

Wilens, T.E., Biederman, J. 'The stimulants,' *Psychiatric Clinics of North America* 1992; 15:191–222.

Jacobvitz, D., Sroufe, L.A., Stewart, M., Leffert, N. 'Treatment of attentional and hyperactivity problems in children with sympathomimetic drugs: A comprehensive review,' *Journal of the American Academy of Child and Adolescent Psychiatry* 1990; 29:677–688.
The above three articles provide comprehensive coverage of the use of stimulant medication in attention deficit disorder.

Tricyclic antidepressants

Ambrosini, P.J., Bianchi, M.D., Rabinovich, H., Elia, J. 'Antidepressant treatments in children and adolescents: II. Anxiety, physical and behavioural disorders,' *Journal of the American Academy of Child and Adolescent Psychiatry* 1993; 32:483–493. *Evaluates the efficacy as well as side effects of the antidepressants in children and adolescents.*

Riddle, M.A., Celler, B., Ryan, N. 'Another sudden death in a child treated with Desiprimine,' *Journal of the American Academy of Child and Adolescent Psychiatry* 1993; 32:792–797. *Includes new information as well as references to all previous case reports and commentaries on this worrying topic.*

Moclobemide (Aurorix)

Trott, G.E., Friese, H.J., Menzel, M., Nissen, G. 'Use of Moclobemide in children with attention deficit hyperactivity disorder,' *Psychopharmacology* 1992; 106:S134–S136.
One of the first reports on the usefulness of Moclobemide (Aurorix) for the treatment of 12 children with ADD in an open trial with documented improvement in parent assessment of behaviour, computer-based assessment of attention and memory function and overall reduction in frontal lobe delta activity on

brain mapping. Moclobemide appeared to be well tolerated with only vague gastric intestinal symptoms reported.

Allergy, food additives and hyperactivity

Conners, C.K. 'Food additives and hyperactive children,' *New York, Plenum Press* 1980.
Reports a 5 per cent success rate in the dietary management of hyperactive behaviours.

Egger, J., Stolla, A., McEwen, L.M. 'Controlled trial of hypo-sensitisation in children with food-induced hyperkinetic syndrome,' *Lancet* 1992; 339:1150–1153.
An exclusion diet (which is nutritionally inadequate and requires vitamin and mineral supplementation) and re-challenge are required to properly diagnose food intolerance in hyperkinesis. This group of researchers previously found that about 60 per cent of children with hyperkinetic syndrome responded to an oligoantigenic diet. Because of the difficulties associated with such restriction diets, hyposensitation using a series of injections was suggested as a means of treating the substantiated food intolerance-induced hyperactivity.

Swain, A.R., Soutter, V.L., Loblay, R.H. *Friendly food: The complete guide to avoiding allergies, additives, and problem chemicals*, Sydney, Murdoch Books 1991.
Explains the process of food intolerance in contributing to the worsening of hyperactive behaviour. Includes lists of foods which are low to very high in food chemicals and suggestions for their use in various recipes.

Pollock, I. 'Hyperactivity and food additives,' *Bibliotheca Nutritio et Dieta* 1991; 48:81–89.
Notable for its excellent reference list of books and scientific studies performed so far on the topic.

Ferguson, A. 'Definitions and diagnosis of food intolerance and

food allergy: Consensus and controversy,' *Journal of Pediatrics* 1992; 121:S7–S11.
Defines the scope of food sensitivities (which is wider than commonly perceived). Hyperactivity appears not to be mediated by allergic but by pharmacologic mechanisms. Foods are thought not to be a component of this disorder in most patients.

McGee, R., Stanton, W.R., Sears, M.R. 'Allergic disorders and Attention Deficit Disorder in children,' *Journal of Abnormal Child Psychology* 1993; 21:79–88.
Large study of 1037 children which calls into question the relationship between attention deficit hyperactivity disorder and allergic disorders.

Wolraich, M.L., Lindgren, S.D., Stumbo, P.J., et al. 'Effects of diets high in sucrose or aspartame on the behaviour and cognitive performance of children,' The New England Journal of Medicine 1994; 330:301–307.
Even when sucrose and aspartame, previously reported to produce hyperactivity in children, are taken in excess, they neither affected the children's behaviour nor cognitive function.

Feingold, B.F. *Why your child is hyperactive*, Random House, New York, 1975.
The original book giving rise to the Feingold diet.

Rapp, D.J. *Allergies and the hyperactive child*. Thorsons Publishing Group, England, 1988.
A pro-dietary management for hyperactivity book, with suggested diets and recipes for those who may want to give it a go.

Reading

Vellutino, F.R., 'Toward an understanding of dyslexia: Psychological factors in specific reading disability,' In Benton, A.L., Pearl, D. (Eds). *Dyslexia: An appraisal of current knowledge.* Oxford University Press, New York, 1977 (pp 61-111).

Pennington, B.F., Van Orden, G.C., Smith, S.D., et al. 'Phonological processing skills and deficits in adult dyslexics,' *Child Development* 1990; pp 1753–1778.

Siegel, L.S., Ryan, E.B. 'Development of grammatical-sensitivity, phonological, and short-term memory skills in normally achieving and learning disabled children,' *Developmental Psychology* 1988; 24:28–37.

The above three references look at the underlying deficits in reading disability.

Noell, E.A. 'Reading,' in Wren, C.T. (Ed), *Language learning disabilities: Diagnosis and remediation*. USA, 1983 (pp 243–295).

Looks at the process of learning to read in normal and reading-disabled children. It provides a framework for diagnosis and remediation of reading.

Spelling and handwriting

Goswami, U. 'Annotation: Phonological factors in spelling development,' *Journal of Child Psychology and Psychiatry* 1992; 33:967–975.

Emphasises the importance of phonological ability in spelling proficiency.

Major, S.T. 'Written language,' in Wren, C.T. (Ed), *Language learning disabilities: Diagnosis and remediation*. USA, 1983 (pp 297–325).

Discusses the underlying processes necessary for proficient spelling and handwriting and includes a framework for assessment and remediation of written language problems.

Sandler, A.D., Watson, T.E., Footo, M., et al. 'Neurodevelopmental study of writing disorders in middle childhood,' *Journal of Developmental and Behavioural Pediatrics* 1992; 13:17–23.

Defines four empirically derived subtypes of writing disorders.

Arithmetic

Shalev, R., Manor, O., Amir, N., Gross-Tsur, V. 'The acquisition of arithmetic in normal children: Assessment by a cognitive model of dyscalculia,' *Developmental Medicine and Child Neurology* 1993; 35:539–601.
Examines a model of arithmetic processing and calculation, which is known to be valid in describing adults with acquired dyscalculia, for its usefulness in the study of the development of arithmetic knowledge in normal children and in children with dyscalculia.

Levine, M.D., Lindsay, R.L., Reed, M.S. 'The wrath of math: Deficiencies of mathematical mastery in the school child,' *Pediatric Clinics of North America* 1992; 39:525–536.
Describes the skills required for mathematical proficiency and approaches to evaluating and managing mathematics underachievement.

Shalev, R.S., Gross-Tsur, V. 'Developmental dyscalculia and medical assessment,' *Journal of learning disabilities* 1993; 26:134–137.
It is suggested that children who are not improving academically in spite of appropriate professional intervention be referred for medical assessment as certain medical conditions including attention deficit disorder without hyperactivity which have a direct bearing on the children's cognitive disability and remedial programs may have been missed.

The study of brainwaves

John, E.R., Prichep, L.S., Fridman, J., Easton, P. 'Neurometrics: Computer-assisted differential diagnosis of brain dysfunctions,' *Science* 1988; 239:162–169.
Describes the methodology used in the creation of topographic brain maps in neurometrics—a computer assisted quantitative

analysis of the electroencephalogram (EEG). Neurometrics may be used as an adjunct to clinical diagnosis.

John, E.R. 'Principals of neurometrics,' *American Journal of EEG Technology* 1990; 30:251–266.
Describes the statistical measures used in obtaining the quantitative analysis of the EEG or event-related potentials which demonstrate consistent patterns of abnormalities in patients with subtle cognitive dysfunctions and in psychiatric disorders.

Nuwer, M.R. 'Quantitative EEG: II. Frequency analysis and topographic mapping in clinical settings,' *Journal of Clinical Neurophysiology* 1988; 5:45–85.
A review of the use of quantitative EEG techniques in clinical settings finds that these tests require substantial user expertise in EEG. For dyslexia there was still no consensus about how to use these tests for individual patient care.

Drake Jr., M.E. 'Clinical utility of event-related potentials in neurology and psychiatry,' *Seminars in Neurology* 1990; 10:196–201.
P_{300} and other commonly described event-related potentials are explained in regard to their origins, the factors which influence them and the neuropsychological processes they are assumed to measure.

Klorman, R. 'Cognitive event-related potentials in attention deficit disorder,' *Journal of Learning Disabilities* 1991; 24:130–140.
A review of the P_{300} event-related potential component in ADD and how it is altered by stimulant medication.

Brain networks in ADD

Mesulam, M-M. 'Large-scale neurocognitive networks and distributed processing for attention, language, and memory,' *Annals of Neurology* 1990; 28:597–613.

An in-depth exposition on the relationship between brain structure and complex behaviours including selective attention, memory and language.

Hynd, G.W., Semrud-Clikeman, M., Lorys, A.R., et al. 'Brain morphology in developmental dyslexia and attention deficit disorder/hyperactivity,' *Archives of Neurology* 1990; 47:919–926.
Metric measurements on magnetic resonance imaging (MRI) scans of the brains of dyslexic and ADD children showed significantly smaller right anterior with measurements than normal. The dyslexics, but not children with ADD, had an increased incidence of reversed asymmetry of the planum-temporale, the auditory association cortex.

Heilman, K.M., Voeller, K.K.S., Nadeau, S.E. 'A possible pathophysiologic substrate of attention deficit disorder/hyperactivity,' *Journal of Child Neurology* 1991; 6:S76–S79.
Looks at the evidence for the neuroanatomical localisation of features characteristic of ADD to the frontal lobe and striatum.

Comorbidity

Semrud-Clikeman, M., Biederman, J., Sprich-Buckminster, S., et al. 'Comorbidity between ADHD and learning disability: A review and report in a clinically referred sample,' *Journal of the American Academy of Child and Adolescent Psychiatry* 1992; 31:439–448.
This contains a review of the studies into the overlap between attention deficit disorder and learning disability. It finds that a wide range of overlap has been reported in the literature (from 10 per cent to 92 per cent).

Biederman, J., Newcorn, J., Sprich, S. 'Comorbidity of attention deficit hyperactivity disorder with conduct, depressive, anxiety, and other disorders,' *American Journal of Psychiatry* 1991; 148:564–577.

Looks at the evidence for the co-occurrence of ADD with conduct disorder, oppositional defiant disorder, mood disorder, anxiety disorder and learning disorder in children — random coincidence or specific comorbidity?

Shaywitz, B.A., Shaywitz, S.E. 'Comorbidity: A critical issue in attention deficit disorder,' *Journal of Child Neurology* 1991; 6:S13–S20.

Examines relationships between ADD, learning disability, conduct disorder and oppositional defiant disorder in regard to issues of definition, prevalence, prognosis and the differences between hyperactive versus non-hyperactive ADD.

August, G.J., Garfinkel, B.D. 'Behavioural and cognitive subtypes of ADHD,' *Journal of the American Academy of Child and Adolescent Psychiatry* 1989; 28:739–748.

Describes how children with ADD and reading disability differ in linguistic and cognitive processes from children with ADD alone. The former exhibit information processing deficits that involve inadequate encoding and retrieval of linguistic information, which are not found in the latter.

Conduct and Oppositional Defiant Disorders

Lahey, B.B., Loeber, R., Quay, H.C., et al. 'Oppositional defiant and conduct disorders: Issues to be resolved for DSM–IV,' *Journal of the American Academy of Child and Adolescent Psychiatry* 1992; 31:539–546.

Oppositional defiant and conduct disorders are seen as overlapping but separate disorders which are staged developmentally as well as in order of severity. Conduct Disorder is more likely to be associated with school suspension, police contact and a family history of antisocial behaviour.

McMahon, R.J., Forehand, R. 'Conduct disorders,' In Mash, E.J. & Terdal, L.J. (Eds), *Behavioural assessment of childhood disorders*, Guilford Press, New York, second edition 1988; 105–153.

McMahon, R.J., Wells, K.C. 'Conduct disorders,' In Mash, E.J. & Barkley R.A. (Eds), *Treatment of childhood disorders*. Guilford Press, New York, 1989 (pp 73–132).
These are two complementary chapters on conduct disorders. Covers the topic of conduct disorders for the practitioner.

Family-genetic transmission of ADD

Biederman, J., Faraone, S.V., Keenan, K., et al. 'Further evidence for family-genetic risk factors in attention deficit hyperactivity disorder: Patterns of comorbidity in probands and relatives in psychiatrically and pediatrically preferred samples,' *Archives of General Psychiatry* 1992; 49:728–738.
The relatives of children with ADD with or without learning disability had higher risk of ADD while the risk of learning disability was higher only among relatives of children with both ADD and a learning disability.

Faraone, S.V., Biederman, J., Lehman, B.K., et al. 'Evidence for the independent familial transmission of attention deficit hyperactivity disorder and learning disabilities: Results from a family genetic study,' *American Journal of Psychiatry* 1993; 150:891–895.
The risk for learning disabilities was highest among relatives of probands with both attention deficit hyperactivity disorder and learning disabilities. The two disorders did not co-segregate in families but their co-occurrence was attributed to non-random meeting between spouses with attention deficit hyperactivity disorder and learning disabilities.

Gillis, J.J., Gilger, J.W., Pennington, B.F., DeFries, J.C. 'Attention deficit disorder in reading-disabled twins: Evidence for a genetic aetiology,' *Journal of Abnormal Child Psychology* 1992; 20:303–315.

Analysis of questionnaire data for attention and hyperactivity symptoms suggest that ADD is highly heritable with a concordance rate of 79 per cent for monozygotic twins and 32 per cent for dizygotic twins. On a scale of 0-1.00, the obtained estimates of the extent to which ADD is heritable is 0.98 ±0.26.

Frontal lobe tests in ADD

Barkley, R.A., Grodzinsky, G., DuPaul, G.J. 'Frontal lobe functions in attention deficit disorder with and without hyperactivity: A review and research report,' *Journal of Abnormal Child Psychology* 1992; 20:163–188.

Some measures presumed to assess frontal lobe dysfunctions were not sensitive to the deficits in ADD. Both types of ADD share some similarities in deficits on frontal lobe tests, while the ADD without hyperactivity group may have an additional problem with perceptual-motor speed and processing.

Shue, K.L., Douglas, V.I. 'Attention deficit hyperactivity disorder and the frontal lobe syndrome,' *Brain and Cognition* 1992; 20:104–124.

ADD children are found to have frontal lobe deficits in motor control and problem solving skills.

The action of neurotransmitters in ADD

Shenker, A. 'The mechanism of action of drugs used to treat attention-defict hyperactivity disorder: Focus on catecholamine receptor pharmacology,' *Advances in Pediatrics* 1992; 39:337–382.

The article reviews in-depth the role of chemical messengers between the cells of the brain in relation to attention deficit disorder. It also describes an innovative method of studying neurotransmitter function in ADD by observing the behavioural effects of different classes of medication—the so called 'pharmacological dissection' of ADD.

Zametkin, A.J., Rapoport, J.L. 'Neurobiology of attention deficit disorder with hyperactivity: Where have we come in 50 years?,' *Journal of the American Academy of Child and Adolescent Psychiatry* 1987; 26:676–686.
A review of the studies into the neurotransmitter defect hypothesis in ADD finds that no single current model can account for the efficacy of all the drugs used in ADD.

PET and SPECT scans in ADD

Lou, H.C., Henriksen, L., Bruhn, P. 'Focal cerebral hypoperfusion in children with dysphasia and/or attention deficit disorder,' *Archives of Neurology* 1984; 41:825–829.
Using Xenon-133 Single Photon Emission Computed Tomography (SPECT), focal areas of low metabolic activity were seen in both perisylvian regions of children with dysphasia and in the white matter of the frontal lobes and caudate nuclei region of patients with ADD. Methylphenidate increased perfusion in the central region, including the basal ganglia and decreased perfusion of motor and primary sensorycortical areas.

Lou, H.C., Henriksen, L., Bruhn, P., et al. 'Striatal dysfunction in attention deficit and hyperkinetic disorder,' *Archives of Neurology* 1989; 46:48–52.
Using Xenon-133 SPECT scans to examine regional cerebral blood flow in 13 children with ADD, it was found the striatal regions were underperfused while the primary sensory and sensorimotor cortical regions were highly perfused. Methylphenidate increased flow to the striatal region and decreased flow to the sensory regions.

Lou, H.C., Henriksen, L., Bruhn, P. 'Focal cerebral dysfunction in developmental learning disabilities,' *Lancet* 1990; 335:8–11.
Xenon 133 SPECT scans differentiated between children with pure ADD (who had low regional cerebral blood flow to the striatal and posterior periventricular regions and high blood flow to the occipital region) and those with a language-learning disability (who had low blood flow to the left temporofrontal regions.

Zametkin, A.J., Nordahl, T.E., Gross, M., et al. 'Cerebral glucose metabolism in adults with hyperactivity of childhood onset,' *The New England Journal of Medicine* 1990; 20:1361–1366.
Positron Emission Tomography (PET) was used to measure glucose metabolism in different regions of the brain of adults with histories of hyperactivity from childhood, who continue to have symptoms and who were also the biologic parents of an ADD child. Glucose metabolism was found to be significantly reduced in the premotor cortex and the superior prefrontal cortex, areas believed to be involved in the control of attention and motor activity.

Controversial therapies for ADD

Silver, L.B. 'Controversial approaches to treating learning disabilities and attention deficit disorder,' *American Journal of Diseases for Children* 1986; 140:1045–1052.
Reviews the literature related to the generally acceptable and the controversial approaches to treatment of learning disabilities and attention deficit disorder. The controversial approaches covered include neurophysiologic retraining (patterning, optometric visual training, and vestibular dysfunction) and orthomolecular medicine (mega vitamins, trace elements,

hypoglycaemia, food additives and preservatives, and refined sugars).

Kaplan, B.J., Polatajko, H.J., Wilson, B.N., Faris, P.D. 'Reexamination of sensory integration treatment: a combination of two efficacy studies,' *Journal Learning Disabilities* 1993; 26:342–7.
Sensory integration was found not to have significant therapeutic advantage over the more simple traditional interventions.

'Learning Disabilities, Dyslexia and Vision. American Academy of Pediatrics Policy Statement,' *Pediatrics* 1992; 90:2–3.
On 23 May 1994, The Australian College of Paediatrics endorsed the policy statement, Learning Disabilities, Dyslexia and Vision, prepared by the American Academy of Pediatrics on this subject. (Information via the Australian College of Paediatrics PO Box 30, Parkville, Victoria 3052.)

Tinted lenses

Cotton, M.M., Evans, K.M. 'A review of the use of Irlen (tinted) lenses,' *Australian and New Zealand Journal of Ophthalmology* 1990; 18:307–312.
Finds much confusion and inconsistency between the many research studies (many of which are unpublished) into the efficacy of tinted lenses and coloured overlays for the treatment of reading disability. Recent experimental evaluations do not support the use of the lenses as a useful intervention for children with reading disabilities.

Help for Parents

A Note to Parents

In our support groups we are constantly contacted by scores of parents, who are concerned that their children have ADD. A few are fortunate in receiving good help, but most tell us they come up against a wall of professionals, who are unbelieving and often obstructive.

As parents it seems unbelievable that attitudes to ADD differ so much on these small islands compared to other parts of the world. We are not suggesting that every badly behaved child or school failure is cause by ADD. All we ask is that children with a major degree of ADD are recognised and afforded the same standard of treatment that is expected in almost every other part of the English speaking world.

If your child's behaviour and learning problems start to make sense as you read this book don't let the matter stop there. In conjunction with your support group, keep lobbying your doctors, teachers and psychologists. If you are told the condition does not exist, this is clearly untrue. You must insist on your right to be referred to someone who has more up to date ideas. The professionals in Canada, Australia, South Africa and USA can't all be wrong, there has to be something we are missing.

The understanding of ADD is about to change dramatically in this country and it is we, the parents, who will bring about this revelation. ADD is no trivial condition, it places immense stress on families and may leave our children poorly educated, unhappy and lacking self esteem. Our children are important, they deserve better.

Gillian Mead
President and Founder Member
The ADD/ADHD Family Support Groups UK

March 1995

Note: The authors believe the following contacts to be correct as of November 1995. As these groups are run by volunteers the positions will change from time to time and the list will go out of date. We will attempt to revise this section at each reprint. We urge everyone using the list to respect the time and privacy of those listed.

The ADD/ADHD Family Support Groups UK

President: Mrs Gill Mead, 1a High St, Dilton Marsh, Westbury, Wilts BA13 4DL.
Telephone: 01373 826045

Chairman: Mr Brian Tuffill, 93 Avon Rd, Devizes, Wilts SN10 1PT.
Telephone: 01380 726710

Below are names and addresses within the organisation of the ADD/ADHD Family Support Groups UK:

Bristol & Weston Super Mare	01934 518779	Elaine Astle
Bath	01761 436579	Moira Woodland
Bedfordshire	01582 861814	Mrs Taylor
Buckinghamshire	01494 716203	Ann Palmer
Cornwall	01726 816596	Julia Haywood
Devon	01752 346105	Jackie King
Glasgow	01419 540569	Mrs Blackie
Gloucester	01242 576760	Angela Kettlety
Hampshire, Farnborough	01252 512707	Kim Fuller
Hampshire, Gosport	01705 521962	Cathy Jackson
Isle of Wight	01983 853648	Valerie Ross
Isle of Wight	01983 852530	Helen Williams
Lancashire	01253 293079	Barbara Worrall
Leicester	0116 2811781	Jackie Rayson
Liverpool	0151 4284037	Anne Holywell
Manchester	0161 7905272	Chris McLanachan
Milton Keynes	01908 679107	Sally Wason
Northumberland	01670 789086	Gill Priest
Suffolk	01440 704151	Lea Potter
Surrey	0181 3929292	Pat Allison (9am–5pm)
Somerset	01460 66037	Eileen Dukes
Tyne & Wear	0191 4153482	Pat Heron
Wales, South	01446 793962	Gail Williams

ADD/ADHD Family Support Group Surrey

01483 418398   Sharon Hawkins
01483 823377   Jannette Hornbrook

ADD Support Group North London

0181 9586727   Andrea Bilbow

The ADHD Support Group

01342 311033   Mrs L Reimer, 15 Harmans Mead, East
Grinstead, Sussex

The Hyperactive Children's Support Group of Ireland

(0)1 2889766 Area code (00) 353 outside Ireland
Contact: Stephanie Mahony

National Support Group

0181 543800   Mr S Mould, LADDER, 142 Mostyn Rd,
London SW19 3LR

LADDER (The National Learning and Attention Deficit Disorders Association), is a national charity, set up in 1993 to serve adults and children with ADD. LADDER is constantly expanding its resource lists to provide names of UK professionals and organisations who understand and treat ADD. This group gives support, advice and promotes awareness of the needs of those with ADD.

APPENDIX XX

TOUGHLOVE—a Self-help Program for Parents Troubled by Teenage Behaviour

The *TOUGHLOVE* program is unfortunately not available in the UK at the time of publication. It was founded by Phyllis and David York in 1972. The Yorks worked as family and youth counsellors in Pennsylvania for 13 years before they realised that while understanding and forgiveness may be commendable, when dealing with children who are constantly in trouble, this approach does not always work.

TOUGHLOVE is a loving solution for families that are being torn apart by unacceptable adolescent behaviour. These young people may skip school, run away from home, abuse drugs or alcohol, get into trouble with the law, get involved with others only on their own terms, or act as though they are the only people to be considered when making decisions about their lives. *TOUGHLOVE* encourages parents to allow their children to experience the natural and logical consequences of their actions. *TOUGHLOVE* also teaches parents that constantly rescuing children from these consequences is not helping them to grow and mature. It is in fact hindering the growth of mature, responsible attitudes.

TOUGHLOVE is tough on parents. It is recognised that it is hard work changing behaviour and habits that have developed over years and that we need the support of others to do this. Parents come to *TOUGHLOVE* because they love their children enough to want to make positive changes in their own lives and in the lives of their children.

TOUGHLOVE is not a parenting program, it is a crisis intervention program.

TOUGHLOVE is a philosophy based on action. Parents join local *TOUGHLOVE* groups for practical and emotional peer support. Parents provide understanding for one another without becoming involved in blaming. *TOUGH*LOVE is non-judgmental. Where counselling or therapy is required, parents are referred to professionals while continuing to get support from the *TOUGH*LOVE group.

*TOUGH*LOVE is also confrontational. Parents are challenged to view themselves clearly, to examine their present behavioural responses and ideas and, where necessary, to make constructive changes. Practical solutions are provided to help change behaviour. It is accepted that the only people that we can change are ourselves and that others may, or may not, choose to change in response to the changes we make. Decisiveness and directness are encouraged. Parents are able to call upon other members of the group for practical support at any time. Members have been asked, at times, to take in children from other families and provide them with temporary shelter while a family tries to resolve a crisis.

*TOUGH*LOVE recognises that it takes a lot of courage to ask for support and that asking is not a sign of weakness. It also requires a degree of commitment so that members give as well as receive. It is recognised that the best solutions to problems come from practical experience. People who have benefited from *TOUGH*LOVE are asked to stay on and help others overcome their problems.

*TOUGH*LOVE is a non-profit organisation offering self-help materials to parents, kids in trouble and professionals working with them. *TOUGH*LOVE groups are not run by professionals. They are run by parents. People in service roles in society may initiate groups but they only survive if the parents are committed to the group and to each other. For many people, *TOUGH*LOVE provides an extended family of caring adults who are not only ready and willing to listen but who are also willing to become involved and *remain* involved.

Recommended reading

*TOUGH*LOVE, Bantam, USA, 1983

*TOUGH*LOVE *SOLUTIONS*, Bantam, USA, 1985

(both are available from bookshops and libraries).

*TOUGH*LOVE: *A self-help manual for parents troubled by teenage behaviour*. 1979. Stock available from *TOUGH*LOVE Auckland.

*TOUGH*LOVE Auckland (Inc.)
31 Uxbridge Road
Howick
Auckland NZ
Ph: (09) 534 7022

Index

Index